ANIMAL SURVIVAL

from camouflage to claws

SCIENCE WITH SIMPLE THINGS SERIES

Conceived and written by
DON BALICK
Edited by
RON MARSON
Illustrated by
PEG MARSON

D1601889

TOPS LEARNING SYSTEMS

342 S Plumas Street
Willows, CA 95988

www.topscience.org

WHAT CAN YOU COPY?

Dear Educator,

Please honor our copyright restrictions. We offer liberal options and guidelines below with the intention of balancing your needs with ours. When you buy these labs and use them for your own teaching, you sustain our work. If you "loan" or circulate copies to others without compensating TOPS, you squeeze us financially, and make it harder for our small non-profit to survive. Our well-being rests in your hands. Please help us keep our low-cost, creative lessons available to students everywhere. Thank you!

PURCHASE, ROYALTY and LICENSE OPTIONS

TEACHERS, HOMESCHOOLERS, LIBRARIES:

We do all we can to keep our prices low. Like any business, we have ongoing expenses to meet. We trust our users to observe the terms of our copyright restrictions. While we prefer that all users purchase their own TOPS labs, we accept that real-life situations sometimes call for flexibility.

Reselling, trading, or loaning our materials is prohibited unless one or both parties contribute an Honor System Royalty as fair compensation for value received. We suggest the following amounts – let your conscience be your guide.

HONOR SYSTEM ROYALTIES: If making copies from a library, or sharing copies with colleagues, please calculate their value at 50 cents per lesson, or 25 cents for homeschoolers. This contribution may be made at our website or by mail (addresses at the bottom of this page). Any additional tax-deductible contributions to make our ongoing work possible will be accepted gratefully and used well.

Please follow through promptly on your good intentions. Stay legal, and do the right thing.

SCHOOLS, DISTRICTS, and HOMESCHOOL CO-OPS:

PURCHASE Option: Order a book in quantities equal to the number of target classrooms or homes, and receive quantity discounts. If you order 5 books or downloads, for example, then you have unrestricted use of this curriculum for any 5 classrooms or families per year for the life of your institution or co-op.

2-9 copies of any title: 90% of current catalog price + shipping.

10+ copies of any title: 80% of current catalog price + shipping.

ROYALTY/LICENSE Option: Purchase just one book or download *plus* photocopy or printing rights for a designated number of classrooms or families. If you pay for 5 additional Licenses, for example, then you have purchased reproduction rights for an entire book or download edition for any **6** classrooms or families per year for the life of your institution or co-op.

1-9 Licenses: 70% of current catalog price per designated classroom or home.

10+ Licenses: 60% of current catalog price per designated classroom or home.

WORKSHOPS and TEACHER TRAINING PROGRAMS:

We are grateful to all of you who spread the word about TOPS. Please limit copies to only those lessons you will be using, and collect all copyrighted materials afterward. No take-home copies, please. Copies of copies are strictly prohibited.

For licensing, honor system royalty payments, contact: **www.TOPScience.org**; or **TOPS Learning Systems 342 S Plumas St, Willows CA 95988**; or inquire at **customerservice@topscience.org**

ISBN 978-0-941008-50-1

CONTENTS

PART I — PREPARATION AND SUPPORT

PART II — ACTIVITIES AND LESSON NOTES

PART III — SUPPLEMENTARY CUTOUTS

A TOPS Teaching Model

If science were only a set of explanations and a collection of facts, you could teach it with blackboard and chalk. You could require students to read chapters in a textbook, assign questions at the end of each chapter, and set periodic written exams to determine what they remember. Science is traditionally taught in this manner. Everybody studies the same information at the same time. Class togetherness is preserved.

But science is more than this. It is also process — a dynamic interaction of rational inquiry and creative play. Scientists probe, poke, handle, observe, question, think up theories, test ideas, jump to conclusions, make mistakes, revise, synthesize, communicate, disagree and discover. Students can understand science as process only if they are free to think and act like scientists, in a classroom that recognizes and honors individual differences.

Science is both a traditional body of knowledge and an individualized process of creative inquiry. Science as process cannot ignore tradition. We stand on the shoulders of those who have gone before. If each generation reinvents the wheel, there is no time to discover the stars. Nor can traditional science continue to evolve and redefine itself without process. Science without this cutting edge of discovery is a static, dead thing.

Here is a teaching model that combines both the content and process of science into an integrated whole. This model, like any scientific theory, must give way over time to new and better ideas. We challenge you to incorporate this TOPS model into your own teaching practice. Change it and make it better so it works for you.

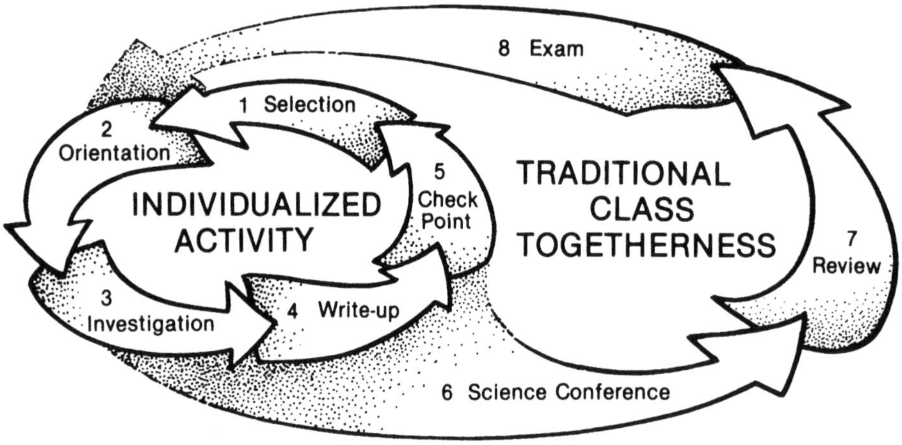

1. SELECTION

Students generally select activity pages in sequence, because new concepts build on old ones in a specific order. There are, however, exceptions to this pattern: students might skip a lesson that is not challenging; repeat an activity with doubtful results; add an experiment to answer their own "what-would-happen-if?" questions.

Working at their own pace, students fall into a natural routine that creates stability and order. They still have questions and problems, to be sure, but remain purposefully engaged with a definite sense of direction.

2. ORIENTATION

Any student with basic reading skills can successfully interpret our carefully designed activity page directions. If your class is new to TOPS, it may take a while for your students to get used to following directions by themselves, and to trust in their own problem-solving ability.

When students ask you for help, first ask them to read what they don't understand. If they didn't read the instruction in the first place, this should clear things up. Identify poor readers in your class. Whey they ask, "What does this mean?" they may be asking in reality, "Will you please read these directions aloud?"

Beyond reading comprehension, certain basic concepts and skills may also be necessary to complete some activity sheets. You can't, for example, expect students to measure the length of something unless they know how to use a ruler as well. Anticipate and teach prerequisite concepts and skills (if any) at the beginning of each class period, before students begin their daily individualized work. Different age groups will require different levels of assistance: primary students will need more introductory support than middle school students; secondary students may require none at all.

3. INVESTIGATION

Students work through the activity pages independently and cooperatively, They follow their own experimental strategies and help each other. Encourage this behavior by helping students only after they have tried to help themselves. As a resource teacher, you work to stay out of the center of attention, responding to student questions rather than posing teacher questions.

Some students will progress more rapidly than others. To finish as a cohesive group, announce well in advance when individualized study will end. Expect to generate a frenzy of activity as students rush to meet your deadline. While slower students finish those core activities you specify, challenge your more advanced students with Extension activities, or to design original experiments.

4. WRITE-UP

Activity pages ask students to explain the how and why of things. Answers may be brief and to the point, with the exception of those that require creative writing. Students may accelerate their pace by completing these reports out of class.

Students may work alone, or in cooperative lab groups. But each one should prepare an original write-up, and bring it to you for approval. Avoid an avalanche of write-ups near the end of the unit by enforcing this simple rule: each write-up must be approved before starting the next activity.

5. CHECK POINT

Student and teacher together evaluate each write-up on a pass/no-pass basis. Thus no time is wasted haggling over grades. If the student has made reasonable effort consistent with individual ability, check off the completed activity on a progress chart. Students keep these in notebooks or assignment folders kept on file in class.

Because the student is present when you evaluate, feedback is immediate and effective. A few moments of your personal attention is surely more effective than tedious margin notes that students may not heed or understand. Remember, you don't have to point out every error. Zero in on particular weaknesses. If reasonable effort is not evident, direct students to make specific improvements and return for a final check.

A responsible lab assistant can double the amount of individual attention each student receives. If he or she is mature and respected by your students, have the assistant check even-numbered write-ups, while you check the odd ones. This will balance the work load and assure equal treatment.

6. SCIENCE CONFERENCE

Individualized study has ended. This is a time for students to come together, to discuss experimental results, to debate and draw conclusions. Slower students learn about the enrichment activities of faster classmates. Those who did original investigations or made unusual discoveries share this information with their peers, just like scientists at a real conference.

This conference is an opportunity to expand ideas, explore relevancy and integrate subject areas. Consider bringing in films, newspaper articles and community speakers. It's a meaningful time to investigate the technological and social implications of the topic you are studying. Make it an event to remember.

7. REVIEW

Does your school have an adopted science textbook? Do parts of your science syllabus still need to be covered? Now is the time to integrate traditional science resources into your overall program. Your students already share a common background of hands-on lab work. With this base of experience, they can now read the text with greater understanding, think and problem-solve more successfully, communicate more effectively.

You might spend just a day here, or an entire week. Finish with a review of major concepts in preparation for the final exam. Our review/test questions provide an excellent resource for discussion and study.

8. EXAM

Use any combination of our review/test questions, plus questions of your own, to determine how well students have mastered the concepts they've been learning.

Now that your class has completed a major TOPS learning cycle, it's time to start fresh with a brand new topic. Those who messed up and got behind don't need to stay there. Everyone begins the new topic on an equal footing. This frequent change of pace encourages your students to work hard, to enjoy what they learn, and thereby grow in scientific literacy.

Getting Ready

Here is a checklist of things to think about and preparations to make before beginning your first lesson on ANIMAL SURVIVAL.

✔ Review the scope and sequence.

Take just a few minutes, right now, to page through all 20 lessons. Pause to read each *Objective* (top left column of the Lesson Notes) and scan each lesson.

✔ Set aside appropriate class time.

Allow an average of perhaps 1 class period per lesson (more for younger students), plus time at the end of this module for discussion, review and testing. If you teach science every day, this module will likely engage your class for about 4 weeks. If your schedule doesn't allow this much science, consult the logic tree on page E to see which activities you can safely omit without breaking conceptual links between lessons.

✔ Number your activity sheet masters.

The small number printed in the top right corner of each page shows its position within the series. If this ordering fits your schedule, copy each number into the blank parentheses next to it. Use pencil, as you may decide to revise, rearrange, add or omit lessons the next time you teach this topic. Insert your own better ideas wherever they fit best, and renumber the sequence. This allows your curriculum to adapt and grow as you do.

✔ Photocopy sets of student activity sheets.

Supply 1 per student, plus supplementary pages as required. Store these in manila folders for convenient access by your students. Please honor our copyright notice at the front of this book. We allow you, the purchaser, to photocopy all permissible materials, as long as you limit the distribution of copies you make to the students you personally teach. Encourage other teachers who want to use this module to purchase their own books. This supports TOPS financially, enabling us to continue publishing new titles for you.

✔ Collect needed materials.

See page D, opposite, for details.

✔ Organize a way to track assignments.

Keep student work on file in class. If you lack a file cabinet, a box with a brick will serve. File folders or notebooks both make suitable assignment organizers. Students will feel a sense of accomplishment as they see their folders grow heavy, or their notebooks fill, with completed assignments. Since all papers stay together, reference and review are facilitated.

Ask students to number a sheet of paper from 1 to 20 and tape it inside the front cover of their folders or notebooks. Track individual progress by initialing lesson numbers as daily assignments pass your check point.

✔ Review safety procedures.

In our litigation-conscious society, we find that publishers are often more committed to protecting themselves from liability suits than protecting students from physical hazards. Lab instructions are too often filled with spurious advisories, cautions and warnings that desensitize students to safety in general. If we cry "Wolf!" too often, real warnings of present danger may go unheeded.

At TOPS we endeavor to use good sense in deciding what students already know (don't stab yourself in the eye) and what they should be told (don't look directly at the sun.) Pointed scissors, pins and such are certainly dangerous in the hands of unsupervised children. Nor can this curriculum anticipate irresponsible behavior or negligence. As the teacher, it is ultimately your responsibility to see that common-sense safety rules are followed; it is your students' responsibility to respect and protect themselves and each other.

✔ Communicate your grading expectations.

Whatever your grading philosophy, your students need to understand how they will be assessed. Here is a scheme that counts individual effort, attitude and overall achievement. We think these three components deserve equal weight:

• Pace (effort): Tally the number of check points and extra credit experiments you have initialed for each student. Low ability students should be able to keep pace with gifted students, since write-ups are evaluated relative to individual performance standards on a pass/no-pass basis. Students with absences, or those who tend to work slowly, might assign themselves more homework out of class.

• Participation (attitude): This is a subjective grade, assigned to measure personal initiative and responsibility. Active participators who work to capacity receive high marks. Inactive onlookers who waste time in class and copy the results of others receive low marks.

• Exam (achievement): Activities point toward generalizations that provide a basis for hypothesizing and predicting. The Review/Test questions beginning on page G will help you assess whether students understand relevant theory and can apply it in a predictive way.

Gathering Materials

Listed below is everything you'll need to teach this module. Buy what you don't already have from your local supermarket, drugstore or hardware store. Ask students to bring recycled materials from home.

Keep this classification key in mind as you review what's needed.

general on-the-shelf materials:	*special in-a-box materials:*
Normal type suggests that these materials are used often. Keep these basics on shelves or in drawers that are readily accessible to your students. The next TOPS module you teach will likely utilize many of these same materials.	Italic type suggests that these materials are unusual. Keep these specialty items in a separate box. After you finish teaching this module, label the box for storage and put it away, ready to use again.
(substituted materials):	*optional materials:
Parentheses enclosing any item suggests a ready substitute. These alternatives may work just as well as the original. Don't be afraid to improvise, to make do with what you have.	An asterisk sets these items apart. They are nice to have, but you can easily live without them. They are probably not worth an extra trip to the store, unless you are gathering other materials as well.

Everything is listed in order of first use. Start gathering at the top of this list and work down. Ask students to bring recycled items from home. The Teaching Notes may occasionally suggest additional *Extensions.* Materials for these optional experiments are listed neither here nor under *Materials.* Read the extension itself to determine what new items, if any, are required.

Quantities depend on how many students you have, how you organize them into activity groups, and how you teach. Decide which of these 3 estimates best applies to you, then adjust quantities up or down as necessary:

$Q_1/Q_2/Q_3$

- **Single Student:** Enough for 1 student to do all the experiments.
- **Individualized Approach:** Enough for 30 students informally working in pairs, all self-paced.
- **Traditional Approach:** Enough for 30 students, organized into pairs, all doing the same lesson.

KEY: *special in-a-box materials* — general on-the-shelf materials — (substituted materials) — *optional materials

$Q_1/Q_2/Q_3$	
1/7/10	rolls cellophane tape
1/30/30	bugs in jars – see notes 3
1/1/1	roll of string
1/10/15	pairs of scissors
various	*classroom animals – see notes 4
1/1/1	box aluminum foil
1/10/15	*large metal washers with 1.5 cm (1/2 inch) diameter holes*
1/2/3	*sets sealable jars of tempera paint in red, blue, yellow, white and black – see notes 9*
1/1/1	box plastic straws
1/30/30	plastic margerine tubs, any color OK
1/30/30	*plastic margarine lids or equivalent, must be white on inside*
1/1/1	sink with running water, or a bucket
1/30/30	*watercolor brushes*
1/7/10	bottles of paste or glue
5/200/200	index cards
1/1/1	*small box cornflakes*
1/1/1	*cassette tape recorders – see notes 16
1/1/1	clock that measures seconds (or substitute wrist watches)
various	*construction materials – see notes 19

Sequencing Activities

This logic tree shows how all the activities in this book tie together. In general, students begin at the trunk of the tree and work up through the related branches. Lower level activities support the ones above.

You may, at your discretion, omit certain activities or change their sequence to meet specific class needs. However, when leaves open vertically into each other, those below logically precede those above, and should not be omitted.

When possible, students should complete the activities in the same sequence as numbered. If time is short, however, or certain students need to catch up, you can use this logic tree to identify concept-related horizontal activities. Some of these might be omitted, since they serve to reinforce learned concepts rather than introduce new ones.

For whatever reason, when you wish to make sequence changes, you'll find this logic tree a valuable reference. Parentheses in the upper right corner of each worksheet allow you total flexibility. They are blank so you can pencil in sequence numbers of your own choosing.

Gaining a Whole Perspective

Science is an interconnected fabric of ideas woven into broad and harmonious patterns. Use extension ideas in the teaching notes plus the outline presented below to help your students grasp the big ideas — to appreciate the fabric of science as a unified whole.

ANIMAL SURVIVAL 37

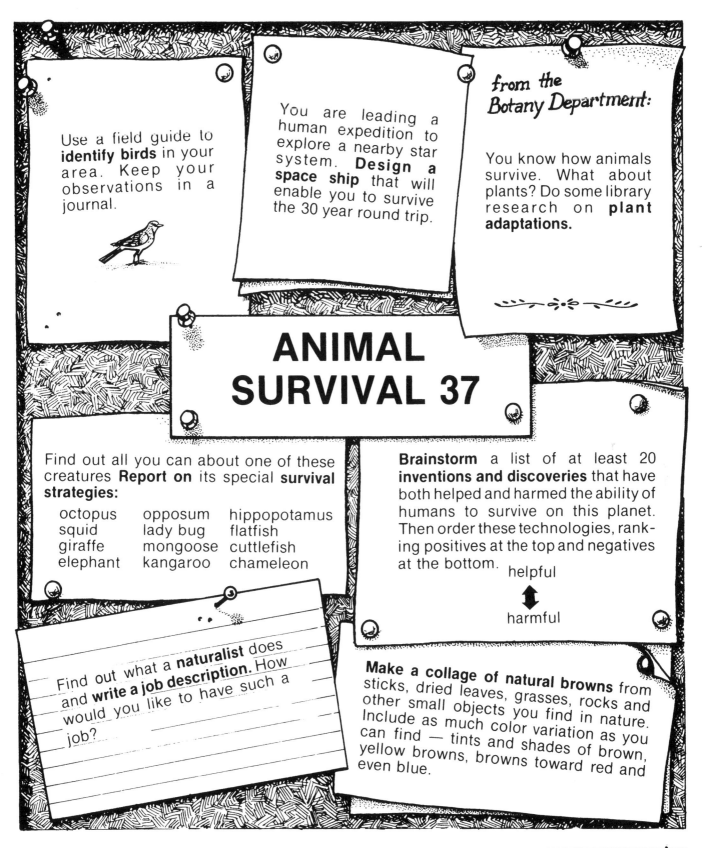

Use a field guide to **identify birds** in your area. Keep your observations in a journal.

You are leading a human expedition to explore a nearby star system. **Design a space ship** that will enable you to survive the 30 year round trip.

from the Botany Department:

You know how animals survive. What about plants? Do some library research on **plant adaptations.**

Find out all you can about one of these creatures **Report on** its special **survival strategies:**

octopus	opposum	hippopotamus
squid	lady bug	flatfish
giraffe	mongoose	cuttlefish
elephant	kangaroo	chameleon

Brainstorm a list of at least 20 **inventions and discoveries** that have both helped and harmed the ability of humans to survive on this planet. Then order these technologies, ranking positives at the top and negatives at the bottom.

helpful

↕

harmful

Find out what a **naturalist** does and **write a job description.** How would you like to have such a job?

Make a collage of natural browns from sticks, dried leaves, grasses, rocks and other small objects you find in nature. Include as much color variation as you can find — tints and shades of brown, yellow browns, browns toward red and even blue.

Review / Test Questions

Photocopy these test questions. Cut out those you wish to use, and tape them onto white paper. Include questions of your own design, as well. Crowd them all onto a single page for students to answer on their own papers, or leave space for student responses after each question, as you wish. Duplicate a class set, and your custom-made test is ready to use. Use leftover questions as a class review in preparation for the final exam.

activity 1

Describe one of your school textbooks using complete sentences. Include its color, size, shape and style, and your personal feelings about it.

activity 2

You are a newspaper reporter who has just seen a UFO. Write a short report for the bureau chief. Make it factual and believable.

activity 3

Compare and contrast your hand with your foot.

activity 4

Look at the clock in your room.

a. Write an observation about this clock.

b. Write an hypothesis about this clock.

activity 5

You are an animal that lives among sharks in the ocean. Draw a body that helps you escape being eaten. Write about how you survive, using complete sentences.

activity 6

Where does this bird likely live, and how does it eat? Explain.

activity 7

Imagine you are a clever rabbit. A coyote has come between you and the safety of your rabbit hole.

a. What is your first response – to escape or confuse? Explain in detail.

b. If your first response fails, what else can you do?

activity 8

Write the correct color in each overlapping space.

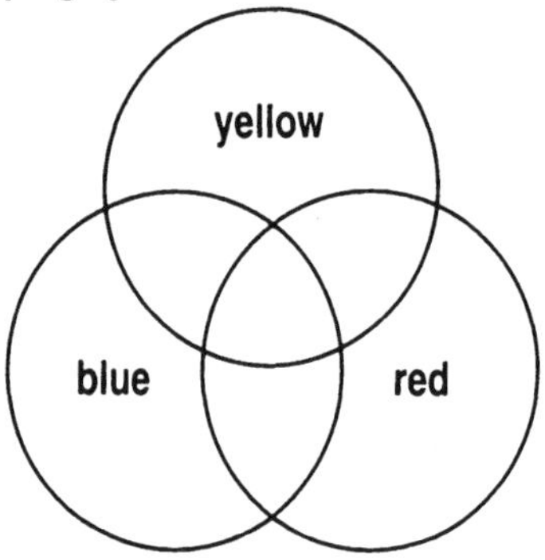

activity 9

If you were painting a landscape, how would you mix ...

a. A shade of green?

b. A tint of brown?

activity 10

Complete each color formula using these letters: (The first is given as an example.)

B = blue
R = red
Y = yellow
W = white
Bk = black

Orange: _R_ + _Y_
Shade of Green: ___+___+___
Shade of Brown: ___+___+___+___
Light Grey: ___+___+___
Pale Pink: ___+___+___

activity 11

Lizards tend to be colored brown, while frogs are colored green. How can you explain this difference in coloration?

activity 12

You are an animal that survives on the school grounds by hiding. What is your most adaptive color? Explain.

activity 13

In England during the industrial revolution, factories burned so much smoky coal that the countryside gradually became darker over a long period of time! How do you think the moths in this area responded to their slowly darkening environment?

activity 14

Imagine you are an insect.

a. Are your chances for survival improved it you mimic a corn flake? Explain.

b. Name something better to mimic. Explain your choice.

activity 15

If a bee stings you and then dies, what good did its warning do?

activity 16

Animals make sounds for many reasons. List four.

activity 17

Reindeer have antlers. Discuss trade-offs for this type of protection.

activity 18

Support both of these statements:

a. Cheetahs can outrun humans.

b. Humans can outrun Cheetahs.

activity 19

a. Circle ONE habitat:

swamp desert forest ocean beach

b. Circe ONE survival strategy:

protective covering speed
warning colors mimicry camouflage

c. Draw a fantasy animal that survives under the conditions you have circled. Explain how it gets food and defends itself.

d. Discuss trade-offs. Explain some disadvantages to your animal's design.

activity 20

Think of behaviors or structures that help different animals survive. Make the list as long as you can.

Answers

activity 1

Evaluate student responses according to effort and completeness of thought.

activity 2

Students should describe the UFO's size, color, shape, speed, direction traveled — any category that a news reporter might use. For example:

At 10:40 P.M. on the night of March 4th, while traveling Route 87, approximately 3 miles west of Bennington, I observed a silver-colored, cigar-shaped, metallic object about the size of an automobile, hovering just above a corn field on the right side of the road. I pulled my car over and stared in amazement. It looked like a space craft of some kind. It remained stationary for perhaps 30 seconds, casting an eerie fluorescent blue light on the corn immediately beneath. Then it moved silently and rapidly to the southeast and disappeared over the horizon.

activity 3

Accept any thoughtful answer that contains both a comparison and a contrast. For example:

My hand and my foot both have 5 digits each. My hand, however, has an opposable thumb that is suitable for grasping, while my foot does not.

activity 4

Here is one possible answer:

a. The second hand sweeps continuously around the clock face.

b. The second hand is driven by an electric motor linked to gears.

activity 5

Accept any answer that thoughtfully explains (in words and pictures) how body structure helps the the fantasy animal survive living among sharks.

activity 6

The bird's long legs are adapted for standing in shallow water; its webbed feet for swimming and standing on soft mud. It likely uses its long neck and shovel-like beak for scooping plants and/or animals from the bottom of shallow ponds.

activity 7

Evaluate for clearness of expression and accuracy of thought. For example:

a. As a clever rabbit, my first response is to stay very still, to use my natural coloration to blend in with my background.

b. If the coyote sees me anyway, I'll hop and dodge and zigzag. Before the coyote can catch me, perhaps I can circle back to the safety of my rabbit hole. If not....

activity 8

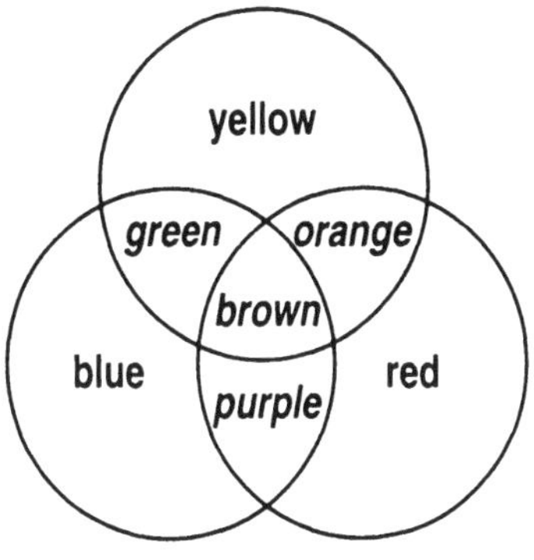

activity 9

a. Mix blue + yellow + black.

b. Mix blue + yellow + red + white

activity 10

Orange: R + Y

Shade of Green: B + Y + Bk

Shade of Brown: R + B + Y + Bk

Light Grey: Bk + W + W

Pale Pink: R + W + W

activity 11

Each animal is adapted to the dominant colors in its own environment. Lizards inhabit dry, desert-brown environments, while frogs live in wet, swampy-green environments.

activity 12

To survive, I should look as much like my environment as possible. My coloration should match the (dust-brown, grass-green, asphalt-grey) of the playground as closely as possible.

activity 13

The moths gradually got darker, too, to better blend in with their changing environment. (More capable students might further explain how this process works: Lighter colored moths were selected (naturally!) by birds more often than darker colored moths because they were easier to see. A greater proportion of darker colored moths survived to pass their more adaptive coloration onto new generations.)

activity 14

a. No. Lots of critters besides people like corn flakes. You stand a good chance of being eaten!

b. Hornets are respected by many creatures as insects to avoid. You would survive much better looking like a hornet.

activity 15

It does that particular bee no good. It does, however, provide you with a memory to avoid bees in the future. All bees you meet in the future are thereby protected.

activity 16

These reasons are all acceptable. Your students may think of others:

- To warn enemies and trespassers.
- To frighten enemies.
- To attract mates.
- To warn other animals in the community of danger.
- To establish dominance in a group.
- To signal young.
- To locate each other.
- To mark territory.

activity 17

Antlers protect reindeer from wolves and other predators. But if a reindeer gets stuck in a tight spot, or if two animals accidently lock horns, they become defenseless against predators and face death by starvation.

activity 18

a. Cheetahs have greater speed. They can run faster than anything on legs if the race covers only a short distance.

b. Humans have greater endurance: the ability to run for many hours at a moderate steady speed. They can outdistance cheetahs if the race is long enough.

activity 19

Evaluate answers according to clarity and completeness of thought.

activity 20

- Flee: run fast, run far, jump, dodge, crawl, fly, glide, dig a hole, swim, dive.
- Hide or confuse: blend in (camouflage), imitate (mimicry), play dead.
- Stay out of reach: dig a hole, climb a tree.
- Warn: sting, taste bad or poisonous, bite, smell bad.
- Weapons: claws, teeth, horns.
- Protection: horns, armor, shells, scales.
- Intimidate: look big, bad and ugly; make a threatening noise.

Long-Range Objectives

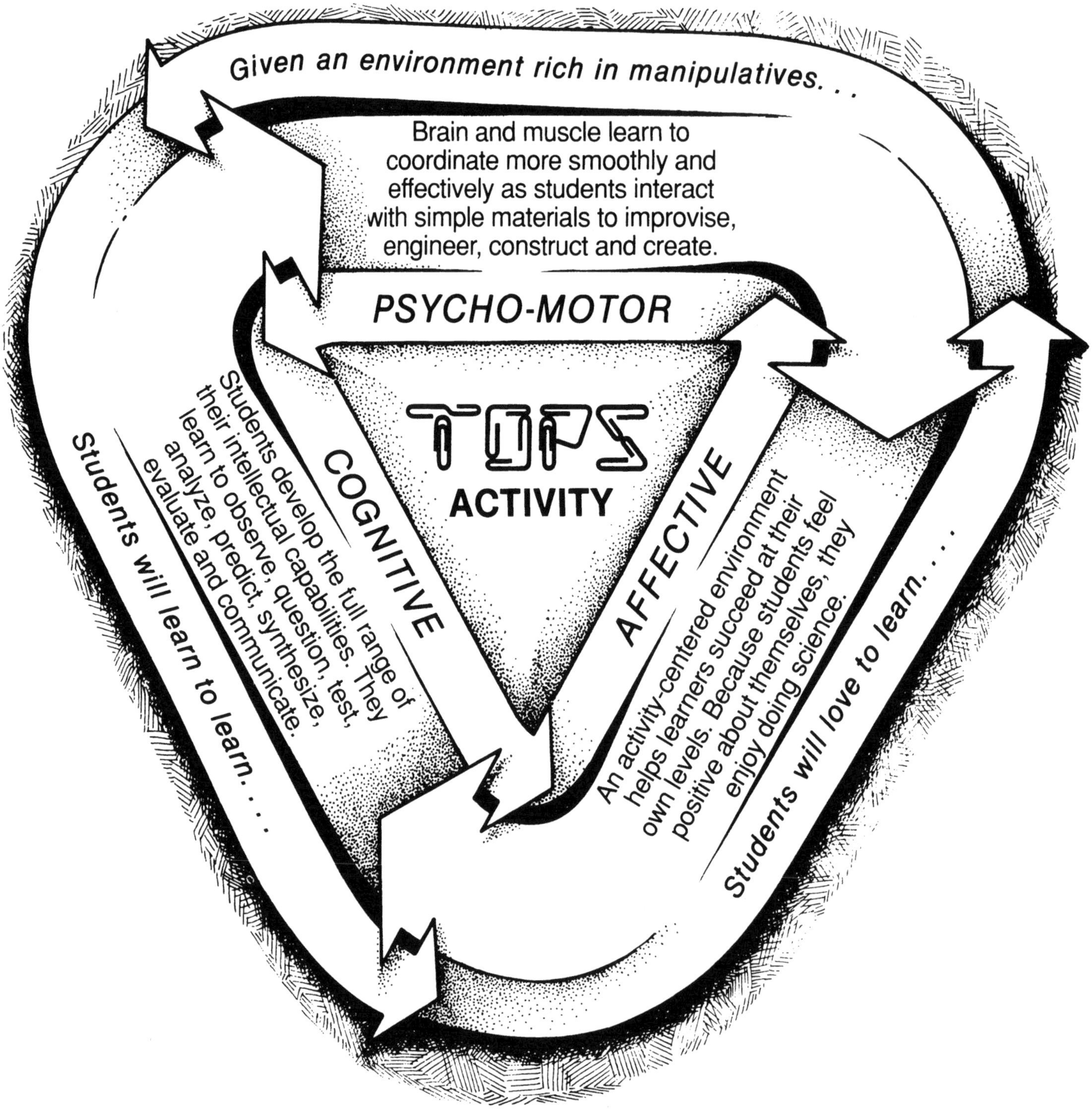

Given an environment rich in manipulatives. . .
Brain and muscle learn to coordinate more smoothly and effectively as students interact with simple materials to improvise, engineer, construct and create.
PSYCHO-MOTOR
TOPS
ACTIVITY
COGNITIVE
Students develop the full range of their intellectual capabilities. They learn to observe, question, test, analyze, predict, synthesize, evaluate and communicate.
Students will learn to learn. . . .
AFFECTIVE
An activity-centered environment helps learners succeed at their own levels. Because students feel positive about themselves, they enjoy doing science.
Students will love to learn. . . .

Teaching to a Higher Level

The activities in this TOPS module, together with your own interaction and guidance as the teacher, can help students grow in many different areas. While **science concepts** *are important, they should not be your only teaching objective. Understanding* **science as process** *is critical if your students are going to mature as independent learners.* **Language skills** *are important to success in all disciplines, and science provides a good context for practice.* **Higher order thinking skills** *are perhaps the most significant, yet most often overlooked. You can take any task to higher levels of thought by careful planning, questioning and modeling. Simple memorization of information is no real advance. To remain at the lowest levels is to encourage future failure.*

Science Concepts

1. Variations exist among individuals of a species.

2. Living things have adaptations that enable them to live in their particular habitats and protect themselves from predators.

3. Animals have characteristics by which they can be described and identified.

4. Animals live in a great variety of habitats. As their bodies adapt to a particular environment they become increasingly specialized, and therefore dependent upon that environment.

5. Scientists look for patterns in what they observe. They develop hypotheses as explanations for the way things are.

6. Repeated observations and measurement improve the reliability of data.

7. Honest, objective reporting is essential to successful work in science.

Science Processes (simple to complex)

1. Observe: use all your senses to know the characteristics of objects and how they interact.

2. Communicate: describe objects and events so that others may learn.

3. Compare: look for similarities and differences among objects and events; measure.

4. Organize: compile, classify and order in a systematic way.

5. Relate: weave together concrete and abstract ideas to test or explain a phenomenon. Use hypothetical modes of inductive and deductive reason.

Language Skills

1. Answer questions using complete sentences, both simple and compound.

2. Present complex ideas in paragraphs that are logically complete. Each paragraph should have a topic sentence, supporting sentences that develop the main idea, plus a summary sentence.

3. Develop and use an outline to effectively coordinate the gathering of information.

4. Proofread material to eliminate errors and refine expression.

Higher Order Thinking Skills

1. INPUT: Information gathering,
- **a.** Use your senses to perceive clearly.
- **b.** Develop a plan to collect information.
- **c.** Label items to aid accuracy, avoid confusion.
- **d.** Use time and space relationships.
- **e.** Use multiple frames of reference.

2. PROCESSING: Making sense from information.
- **a.** Define a problem and determine solutions.
- **b.** Select relevant information.
- **c.** Form a clear image of what you're looking for.
- **d.** Develop a plan.
- **e.** Relate objects, events, and conditions.
- **f.** Separate into categories.
- **g.** Hypothesize.
- **h.** Defend an opinion with logical evidence.
- **i.** Be flexible in using problem-solving strategies.

3. OUTPUT: Applying and evaluating actions.
- **a.** Use precise communication.
- **b.** Accurately express another point of view.
- **c.** Avoid relying only upon trial and error: think the process through.
- **d.** Write thoughtfully. Don't jot down your first idea.
- **e.** Resist panic or despair if solutions are elusive.
- **f.** Review answers for accuracy.

Strive to integrate all four learning components into every lesson you teach. The activities in this TOPS unit encourage this holistic approach: students learn concepts by doing, not by rote; exercises require significant creative expression; questions lead from fact to synthesis. You can eliminate the "I can't do this" syndrome by asking students to identify exactly what they lack in solving the problem. When you help students find the missing information, locate the necessary material, or learn the necessary skill, you're truly teaching. (This is much better than working problems yourself, while students look passively on.) Regular use of journals will also encourage growth. As students actively process information and communicate ideas from one page to the next, personal growth will become apparent, and thereby motivate more complex and sophisticated output.

ACTIVITIES AND LESSON NOTES 1-20

☞ As you duplicate and distribute these activity sheets, **please observe our copyright restrictions** at the front of this book. Our basic rule is: **One book, one teacher.**

☞ TOPS is a small, not-for-profit educational corporation, dedicated to making great science accessible to students everywhere. Our only income is from the sale of these inexpensive modules. If you would like to help spread the word that TOPS is tops, please request multiple copies of our **free TOPS Ideas catalog** to pass on to other educators or student teachers. These offer a variety of sample lessons, plus an order form for your colleagues to purchase their own TOPS modules. Thanks!

TELL ME CLEARLY

1 Take off your shoe and put it on your desk . . .

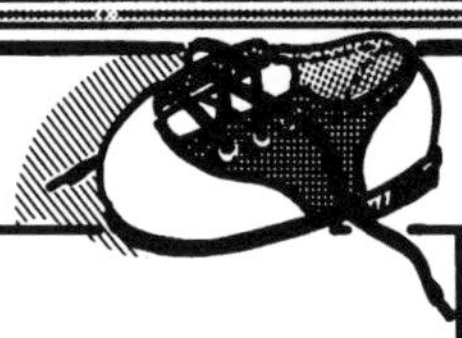

. . . Fill in each box with words that describe your shoe.

A. COLOR	B. SIZE
C. SHAPE AND STYLE	**D. FEELINGS ABOUT SHOE**

2 Describe your shoe in greater detail.
Write **COMPLETE SENTENCES** in each box.

A. Write more about **COLOR:**
Is there a mixture *(blue-green, yellow-green)?* Are there patterns *(stripes, dots)?* Do you notice different shades *(light, dark)?*

B. Say more about **SIZE:**
Measure your shoe with this centimeter ruler. Compare it to something familiar *(As big as a hamburger?)*

C. Be descriptive about **SHAPE** and **STYLE:**
(Athletic shoe or boot? Laces or velcro fasteners? High top? Rubber toe? Left or right?)

D. Amplify your **FEELINGS** about your shoe:
(My only shoe; wonderful shoe; hand-me-down shoe, etc.)

3 Now write a totally wonderful and detailed description of your shoe. Use all your new observations about **color, size, shape and style** and **feelings.**

cm ruler

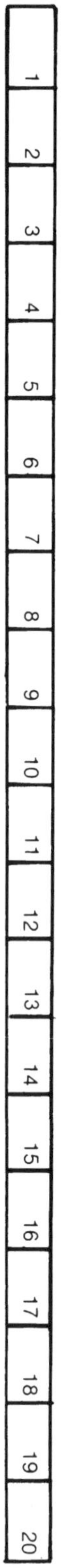

Objective

To sharpen observation and communication skills. To enable students to express themselves at higher levels of thought.

Lesson Notes

1. Things to notice about your shoe, any shoe, generate an endless array of categories. There is nothing special about these particular criteria. (You may change them if you wish!) These categories only define an entry level into the observing process, a level that will challenge and exercise young minds and help them to grow.

2. The broad task of observing your shoe is broken into specific things to notice, both about your shoe and about yourself. (Modern physics places great emphasis on this dynamic interaction between the observer and the observed.) What we are seeking here is an expansion, first of what the observer sees, then an accurate communication of that expanded information.

3. The whole idea is to carry students beyond their first idea, their first response, into deeper levels of thought and self expression. If your students habitually respond with one or two word descriptions that require little or no thought, where is the possibility of real intellectual growth? How can they benefit from activities that require higher order thinking processes?

Answers

1. A one or two word response, the first idea that answers the question, is appropriate here, and here alone. This may be the skill level where many of your students now function. Let new growth begin!

2. Here comes the expansion of initial ideas. Demand complete, thoughtful sentences. Your students will rise to the level of your expectations.

3. This is a synthesis, a grand combination of previous ideas. Students must do more than rewrite the previous 4 sentences, stringing them together with conjunctions.

Write a model answer on the board, illustrating the kind of response you are trying to elicit. For example: These super-sleek blue with green striped, size 7 running shoes have brought me luck at all of our track meets.

Materials

☐ None. Students supply their own shoes.

YOU DON'T SAY

1 **PUZZLE:** What's a 6-inch, 6-sided, yellow-orange, tube-shaped object with one end that undoes the work of the other end?

2 Now you write a similar puzzle about any 3 objects in your room. Describe each object well, but don't give away the answer.

PUZZLE A	PUZZLE B	PUZZLE C

SAVE THESE BOXES FOR YOUR FRIEND'S GUESSES.

A	B	C

3 Secretly write the name of each object in the boxes below.

Write lightly, so your friend can't see through the paper!

4 Cover your answers by folding up along the dotted line, and taping.

5 Trade puzzles with a friend.

Write your best guess in the boxes above, then trade back.

6 How many did your friend guess correctly?

0 out of 3	1 out of 3	2 out of 3	3 out of 3

7 Name some jobs that require you to write accurate descriptions.

police	

A	B	C

FOLD UP AND TAPE

Objective

To learn to see clearly and say it well.

Lesson Notes

This activity, like the last, encourages students to think before they write, to invent clever riddles about common objects in their room. Riddles are not only interesting and fun, writing them involves higher-order communication skills. And solving them is an exercise in thoughtful observation.

1-2. The riddle describes exactly what a pencil looks like and how it functions. When you guess the answer (or otherwise find it out) you realize that it could be nothing else. Encourage your students to write as cleverly, to refine their description so well that it can only apply to one mystery object and no other. Their inventiveness and skill may surprise you.

Monitor your class closely as students select mystery objects and write their secret descriptions about them. Those who need inspiration might consider the four observation categories introduced in the previous shoe activity. There is much to say about any object. There are many ways to say it.

Look out for careless writers and speedsters. Direct them to rewrite more thoughtfully, with greater care. The whole idea is to write subtle and wonderful observations, not to see who can finish first. A good way to prevent students from racing through this activity is to split it into two time frames. Consider assigning steps 1 and 2 first. Save the grading and guessing for later, after everyone has had the chance to finish *and* do a good job.

3-6. Notice that this activity sheet has space for two sets of answers. The one who *composes* the riddles writes the solutions in the boxes at the extreme bottom of the page. (These are then folded up and hidden from view.) The one who *solves* the riddles writes answers just below the riddle boxes, at the bottom of step 2.

As students trade puzzles, try to establish a friendly competitive atmosphere. Just giving the answers to a friend helps no one. You may wish to preselect pairs of students who work well together, or let students exchange with whomever is available. This is probably not the time to pair students with significantly different abilities.

If enthusiasm is still running high, ask for "best riddle" nominations from your class. (No self nominations, please.) Honor clever riddles in a bulletin board "hall of fame." Write down the author's name and mystery description on one side of an index card. Write the solution to the riddle on the opposite side.

Discussion

Who needs to say things accurately? Just about anyone in any profession. Consider these humorous examples. Ask your class to invent others of their own:

A doctor explaining a physical problem to another doctor: "This big red thing looks bad!"

A teacher explaining to a parent that their child needs help. "Well, your kid is really, I don't know, dumb, I guess."

An instructor describing to a recruit how to throw a hand grenade. "Let's see, it's either 5 seconds or 10 seconds."

Answers

1. Pencil.

2-3. Each puzzle will be as unique as the student who writes it. The answers to each puzzle should be included at the bottom, then folded up (out of sight) and taped.

6. Varied results.

7. Possible responses:

police	engineer
surveyor	pharmacist
carpenter	naturalist
astronaut	scientist

Materials

☐ Cellophane tape.

COMPARE / CONTRAST

1 Compare yourself to a bug in a jar.

Identify yourself:

Identify your bug:

List 5 ways you are the **same** as your bug:

List 5 ways you are **different** than your bug:

2 Measure yourself and your bug with this ruler. You may want to use some string as well.

cm ruler

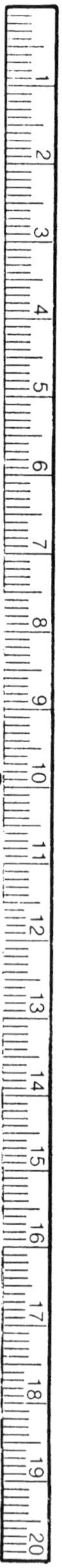

Your Height: ....

Arm Length: ....

Explain how you measured yourself:

Bug's Length: ....

Front Limb Length: ....

Explain how you measured your bug:

3 How many bugs lined up head to tail would equal your height?

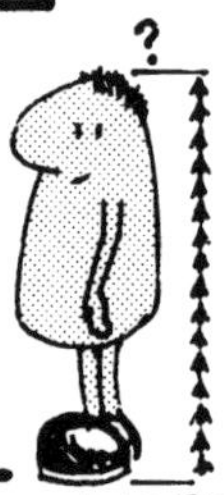

Show your math on the back!

4 If your bug were as tall as you, would its arms be longer or shorter than yours?

Show your math on the back!

Objective

To observe similarities and differences between yourself and another animal.

Lesson Notes

Have each student bring a live bug to school. Ask them to bring it in a small, clean jar with the label removed.

Remind students to treat the critters they catch with due consideration and respect. (If someone put *you* in a jar, how would *you* want to be treated?) They should handle the bugs gently, of course, and keep them captive no longer than necessary. If they need to hold them for more than a few hours, they must ventilate the jar with air holes in the lid, and perhaps add a bit of soil or plant matter to provide moisture and food.

Students who forget to bring a bug to school might pair up with someone who did remember. If your room is a small animal zoo already, perhaps you can spare outside creatures altogether and use your own resources.

1. There are numerous similarities and differences to notice. Size, color, shape, texture, structure, body parts, function, and movement are only some of the possible categories to compare and contrast. Watch out for those who limit their observations to single categories, color, for example: I have blue eyes, it has brown eyes; I have blond hair, it has black hair; I have tan feet..., and so on. Encourage higher, more complex levels of thought and expression whenever possible.

2. An excellent way to introduce your class to a metric ruler is to read up the decimal scale while students trace your progress with their pencil points on their own worksheet rulers: 1.0 cm, 2.0 cm, 4.0 cm, 5.5 cm, 6.9 cm, 8.1 cm.... Skip forward at random intervals until you cross the entire ruler. Your class will appreciate that reading a metric scale is as easy as counting!

The ruler, of course, is not long enough to measure people dimensions. String can help. Just leave some laying around in a few conspicuous places in your classroom. Let your students discover it and figure out how to use it.

Younger students may lose track as they attempt to measure the relatively long string against the shorter 20 cm ruler. Placing successive string segments against the ruler, they must be able to count by 20's — 20 cm, 40 cm, 60 cm, ... until they reach the end of the string, presumably equal to their height. Use this conversion table to detect gross measuring errors, probably caused by confused counting:

4.0 feet = 220 cm
4.5 feet = 137 cm
5.0 feet = 152 cm
5.5 feet = 168 cm
6.0 feet = 183 cm

Its not easy to tape-measure the length of a bug's arm. But you can estimate. Draw a line on paper, for example, that matches the length of the bug's front limb, then measure the length of the line you have drawn. Or cut off part of the ruler and put it in the jar. Perhaps the bug will walk over it and you can catch a quick measurement. Give students the space and freedom to come up with their own solutions.

3-4. These last two steps require students to make quantitative sense of the measurements they have just made, to compare and contrast body size in a meaningful way. Rounding the bug's length off to the nearest whole centimeter will make the problem easy to calculate, but the result may not be too accurate.

Let your class first attempt these problems unassisted. If they need help, write more detailed instructions on your board, like these:

(3) Divide your bug's length into your length to find the ratio (how many times it fits).

(4) Multiply this ratio by the bug's limb length. Is the result longer than your own arm?

As a last resort, work out the problems as a class exercise. Your task as the teacher is to provide the minimum amount of necessary help to enable your students to grow intellectually and experience success.

If any critters look sluggish or sick, ask students to release them in a suitable place on the school grounds, or to take them home and put them back under the rock or log where they were found. If they are active and healthy, consider saving them for the next activity.

Extension

Write an account of where you looked for your bug and how you captured it. What kinds of escape strategies did the bug use to try to get away from you?

Answers

1. Varied answers.

2-3. Sample calculation:
Your Height: 150 cm
Arm Length: 60 cm
Bug's Length: 1 cm
Front Limb Length: 0.5 cm

Number of bugs to equal my height:
150 cm / 1 cm = 150

A bug equal to my height (150 times taller) would need arms 150 times longer to keep its same proportions:
150 times x 0.5 cm = 75 cm

Compared to my arm length of 60 cm, the bug has proportionally longer arms compared to body length.

Materials

☐ A bug in a jar. See opening paragraphs in these Lesson Notes.
☐ String.
☐ Scissors.

OBSERVE / HYPOTHESIZE

Name of animal: **Place observed:** **Date observed:**

1 Describe your animal. Use complete sentences.

COLOR:

SIZE:

SHAPE:

YOUR FEELINGS ABOUT THIS ANIMAL:

2 Draw your animal here. Sketch details accurately.

cm ruler

3 **OBSERVATION:** Take 5 minutes to record everything you notice about how your animal moves and sounds. Write **WHAT** you see or hear, but don't explain it.

(example: **1.** It walks in circles.)

An OBSERVATION describes WHAT happens.

1. ....
2. ....
3. ....
4. ....
5. ....
6. ....
7. ....
8. ....
9. ....
10. ....

4 **HYPOTHESIS:** Try to explain **WHY** the animal moves or sounds like it does. Choose numbers from above, then write your reason.

(example: **1.** It was trying to escape.)

An HYPOTHESIS explains WHY something happens.

....

....

(Please continue on the back.)

Objective

To provide a generalized form useful for observing a diversity of animal life, both in and out of the classroom. To understand the distinction between an observation and an hypothesis.

Lesson Notes

This worksheet invites your class to observe on many levels; to describe and draw animals: to concentrate for 5 uninterrupted minutes on their movements and sounds, recording events as they actually happen; to hypothesize, making sense of behaviors they see

Begin in the classroom. Your students might use the same bugs they used in activity 3, if they are still active. Otherwise, find new specimens: bring in new bugs; observe goldfish in an aquarium; bring in a pet rabbit. Any subject that moves or makes noise is suitable. You can even ask the class to observe you observing them. (A nice way to enjoy 5 minutes of uninterrupted silence!)

Continue outside, on the school grounds. Duplicate another set of activity sheets, pass out clipboards or writing boards, observe animals wherever they can be found. Organize a field trip if you can. Any natural setting will provide a rich variety of things to see and hear to wonder about and explain.

Keep additional activity sheets on hand for assigning independent observations to do at home Students might study the family dog, or make their own foray into a wild place to observe something wonderful. Extra-credit assignments are also possible. Multiple observations could be combined to form part of an ongoing journal. The possibilities for growth are rich indeed, both in science and language arts.

2. Creativity at many levels, graphic as well as verbal, is the goal. If you honor only the spoken word or the written idea, you limit other legitimate ways of knowing. Everyone can draw. It takes time, and serious effort. You must look clearly, process what you see, then output your knowledge in a calm, accurate manner.

Demand as much as students are able to give. Even young students can make large drawings and pay some attention to detail. Encourage older students to specify scale and point of view: top view, side view, etc.

3-4. Five minutes of single-minded concentration, writing down each thing you notice, may seem difficult at first. But it's well worth the effort and practice. As students learn to concentrate and record data, this research skill can begin to eliminate the ancient game of copying from reference books and calling it science.

Here is an interesting way to distinguish between observations and hypotheses. While you have the undivided attention of your entire class, write this sentence on the board: "Why am I writing this?" After a few moments of mysterious silence, erase it.

Ask your students to tell you what you did, sorting out personal speculations from specific observations. Those who are hypothesizing will attempt to answer the question. Those who are observing will not answer the question, but rather, describe you writing it.

Answers

1-4. Observations and hypotheses will be the unique expression of the observer.

Materials

- ☐ An animal to observe. See second paragraph under Lesson Notes.
- ☐ Scissors.

BEAT IT!

Imagine you are standing in an open field. A hungry hunter is looking for you.

1. Draw what you might look like if you could escape into the trees. Explain in a few sentences how your body helps protect you.

Draw and write in these spaces. Use the back if you need more room.

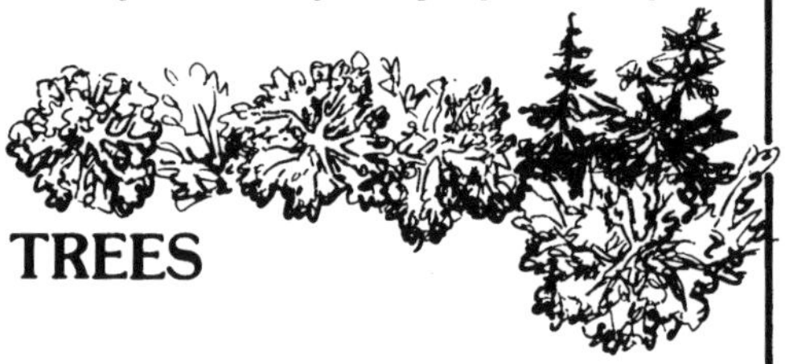

2. Suppose you choose the rocks. Draw yourself as a different animal, and explain in a few sentences how you survive.

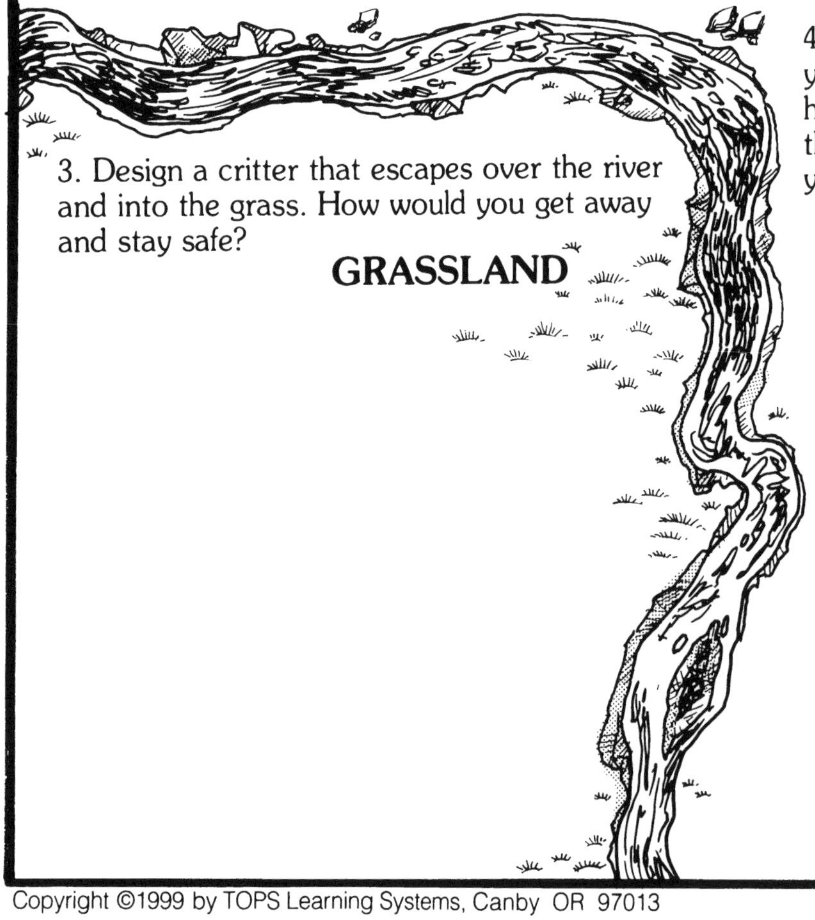

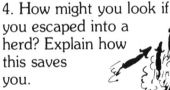

3. Design a critter that escapes over the river and into the grass. How would you get away and stay safe?

4. How might you look if you escaped into a herd? Explain how this saves you.

Objective

To recall the many different ways that animals survive. To relate animal survival strategies to variations in habitat.

Lesson Notes

Your students are free to be any kind of animal they like, real or imagined, as long as they conform to natural law. They can, for example, "disappear" among the trees by looking like a tree, but they can't simply vanish into thin air.

Before you distribute this worksheet, set the scene in a different context. Be dramatic if this suits your personality: imagine you are standing on an ocean beach. A hungry hunter is looking for you! (Don't define the predator.) Change into an animal shape that helps you survive. What would you look like and how do you escape?

Entertain suggestions from the class. Encourage students to describe both a body shape and the resulting benefit. Draw at least one example on your blackboard.

I SCARE AWAY PREDATORS BY RAISING MY CLAWS. IF THAT DOESN'T WORK, I CAN DIG INTO THE SAND TO HIDE.

Now your class is ready to do the activity sheet. Your students are thinking in terms of survival, and you have provided a model answer for them to emulate.

1-4. Encourage your students to consider all their options before deciding on body shapes. They might, for example, take cover in, on, under or among the trees. Identify students who work in haste. Require them to add greater detail to their drawings; to make their written descriptions more complete.

If time allows, ask volunteers to share their answers with the class. After each presentation, ask the rest of the class to vote on each creature's chances for survival.

thumbs up **will survive**

thumbs sideways **may survive**

thumbs down **won't survive**

Discussion

Allow your students to learn from each other. List all the animals they have chosen in each of the four categories. Then identify similarities in body structure or behavior. Example: All these herd animals are large and run fast; they mostly eat plants; they are highly social, etc.

Answers

Sample answers:

1. I'm a monkey. My long legs help me run fast and climb high into the trees. My brown color makes me hard to see.

2. I'm a turtle. Hiding inside my shell among the rocks makes me look just like another rock. And even if I am found, I won't come out of my strong, hard shell.

3. I'm a snake. I'll swim across the river and sneak under the grass where no predator can see me.

4. I'm a zebra. Running with the herd, there will be so many black and white stripes moving in so many directions, predators will get confused.

Materials

None.

ADAPT-A-BIRD

Cut and tape a bird into each habitat.

Cut out body parts that will help each bird survive in its environment.

Explain why you choose certain body parts.

WATER ENVIRONMENT

DENSE FOREST

OPEN SPACES

Objective

To appreciate how each body part helps a bird survive in its particular environment.

Lesson Notes

Introduce this activity by asking your class to imagine for a moment that they are all birds. On scratch paper, have them write down their food of preference, then draw the best possible beak shape to help them easily obtain this food (Long and slender? Blunt and short? Hooked? Curved? Scooped?). Ask volunteers to share their answers with the class.

Emphasize that details are important. The shape of the bird's beak may determine whether it lives or dies!

End your introduction by distributing two pages to your class, both the activity sheet and the body-parts supplement.

Students should piece together a bird for each of the 3 environments, taping body parts directly on each picture (not below it). Precision cutting is not necessary. Even rough cuts work well, outlining the bird in a jagged white background.

If scissors are in short supply, ask half your class to complete the written part of this exercise first while the other half cuts and tapes. If rolls of tape are limited, distribute short pieces yourself, Stick them to the edge of each student's desk as you walk about the room.

Discourage the practice of cutting out all the bird parts first. This is time consuming and unnecessary. Not all parts will be used. Moreover, even a slight breeze could cause great disorder and carry away many of the smaller pieces.

Some of the birds may look ill-conceived Not to worry. More important, does the explanation under each picture justify the selection of body parts in a thoughtful, coherent way? If so, the bird survives!

Answers

Sample answers: **OPEN SPACES**

This bird uses its large wing span to fly high and easy over open spaces looking for small animals. Its feet have claws for clutching prey, and its beak is curved to tear up meat.

DENSE FOREST

This bird is small enough to easily dart in and out of tight spaces among trees. Its body has a camouflaged pattern to blend in. Its feet can grasp small branches. Its short, stout beak enables it to crack open seeds and search out insects.

WATER ENVIRONMENT

This bird stands in shallow water on its long legs. Its webbed feet keep it from sinking into the mud and also help it swim. Its long neck enables it to feed off the bottom, scooping up water plants with its shovel-like beak.

Materials

- ☐ A body parts supplement page.
- ☐ Scissors.
- ☐ Cellophane tape. Don't substitute glue: it makes the bird parts more difficult to accurately fix inside each environment.

STAYING ALIVE

Animals have many ways to survive an attack. Two ways are ESCAPE and CONFUSION.

1 ESCAPE: What kinds of animals would escape in these ways, and where would they live? Answer clearly and completely.

Run:

Hop:

Crawl:

Fly:

Swim:

Glide:

2 CONFUSE: What kinds of animals can use these tricks, and where would they live? Answer clearly and completely.

Is colored like tree bark:

Looks like a leaf or a twig:

Tastes or smells bad:

Has skin that can protect it:

3 Imagine you are any animal above. Complete this **Diary** for one day of your life.

animal .... date ....

Where I went today:

My most exciting experiences:

What I learned to help me survive tomorrow:

Continue on the back...

TOPS LEARNING SYSTEMS

Objective

To study how animals survive using escape and confusion. To appreciate the rich diversity of animal adaptation within these two broad categories.

Lesson Notes

Animal survival strategies are remarkably diverse, even among members of the same species. The jackrabbit runs when danger approaches; the cottontail stays perfectly still and hides. Both are rabbits. This activity attempts to elaborate on this diversity, drawing on each student's background knowledge and personal experience.

1-2. The idea here is to name an animal, any animal that escapes using the specified action; then to describe the kind of habitat where this mode of escape is particularly useful.

1. Running is clear enough. Many herd animals run as their first line of defense: others resort to running if other escape strategies fail. Hopping can include the obvious, or not so obvious: fleas and crickets, for example. Crawling, flying and swimming are easy categories to complete. Gliding may not be as familiar. Gliders glide through the air on winglike parts. They may use wind currents to advantage, but do not fly. Gliders include squirrels, frogs, snakes and spiders and many insects. (With much science fiction programming on the airways, particularly on Saturday morning cartoons, you may need to question some answers.)

2. Confusing behaviors are less common, and therefore harder to specify. Partners can help. Encourage students to brainstorm together. Many insects, moths, toads and snakes, as well as some birds, look like tree bark. Insects are most commonly adapted to look like leaves and twigs. The walking slick is perhaps best known. The names of these creatures are less important than the concept that they have survived by adapting to look like the place where they live. Critters that taste and smell bad include skunks, of course, and other brightly- colored, striped or spotted creatures such as lady bugs or monarch butterflies. Skin protection is a survival strategy employed by a wide variety of spined, horned, armored, shelled or roughly scaled creatures.

3. Creative writing must not be considered incidental or frivolous to the practice of science. Where else but through fantasy can students consider animals outside their immediate experience? Let them take their time with this step and do a good job. There will be humor, or attempts at humor, but funny work can still be excellent.

Consider assigning this part of the lesson as homework, or as independent class work when other activities are completed. If students are compiling their animal observations into an ongoing creative writing journal (a possibility from activity 4), this diary assignment might be included as part of that journal.

Answers

1. Sample answers:

Run: A buffalo. It lives in a herd on the wide open plains.
Hop: A flea. It jumps onto passing animals and lives in their fur.
Crawl: A snake. It lives between rocks and under the cover of grass.
Fly: A housefly. Have you ever tried to swat one?
Swim: A frog. It lives in swamps and dives under water when in danger.
Glide: A squirrel. It lives in the woods. It can leap and glide from tree to tree.

2. Possible answers:

Colored like tree bark: A moth. It rests on the bark of trees.
Looks like leaf or twig: A grasshopper. It lives among grasses and plants.
Tastes or smells bad: A brightly-colored toad. It lives in wet tropical areas.
Protective skin: A porcupine. It lives in the woods.

3. Varied answers.

Materials

None.

STIR CRAZY

1 Tear off some foil about as wide as your hand. Fold it in half.

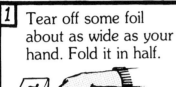

2 Lay the foil over a metal washer. Press into its hole to make 3 small cups.

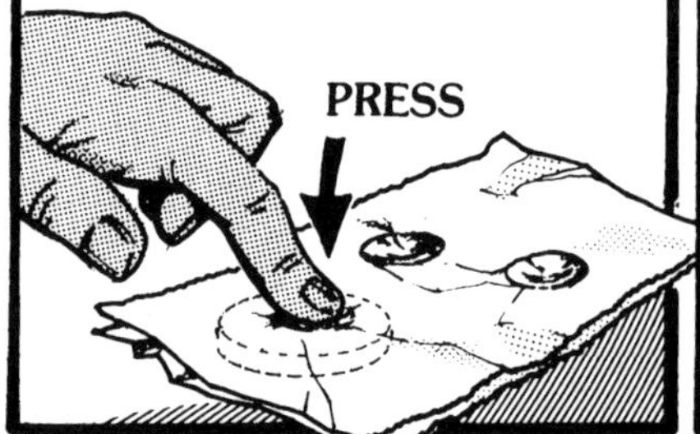

3 Drip these 3 paint colors into the cups.

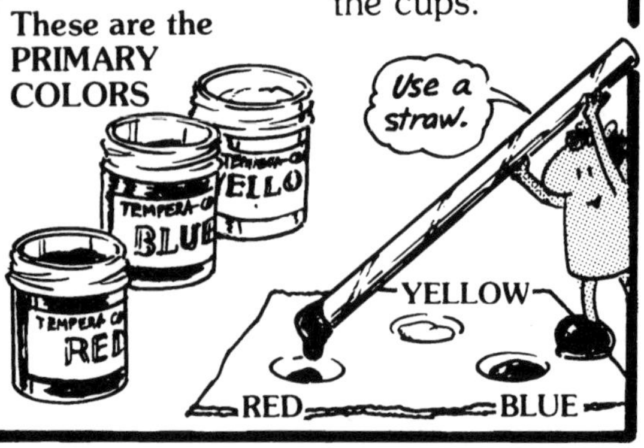

4 Dip your finger into the **red** cup, then touch the paint to a plastic lid.

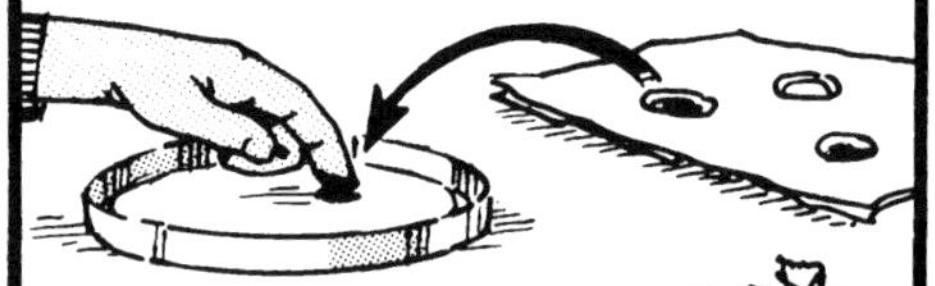

Wipe your finger with a crumpled damp paper towel.

5 Now mix in a dab of **yellow** . . .

. . . and finger-paint a sample in this oval.

FORMULA: R+Y

COLOR SAMPLE: ( )

...KEEP GOING...

Mix in more yellow on your lid, following this formula:

... +Y

... +Y

... +Y

Make COLOR SAMPLES as you go.

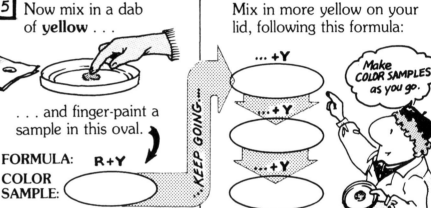

6 Mix these colors on clean areas of your **palette.**

B+Y	R+B	R+B	...+Y
( )	( )	( )	( )
....+Y	...+ water	...+Y	...+water
( )	( )	( )	( )
...+Y	...+water	...+Y	...+water
( )	( )	( )	( )

...KEEP GOING...

7 Write the correct **PRIMARY** color in each box: **RED, YELLOW,** or **BLUE.**

PRIMARY COLORS				SECONDARY COLORS
	+		=	
	+		=	
	+		=	

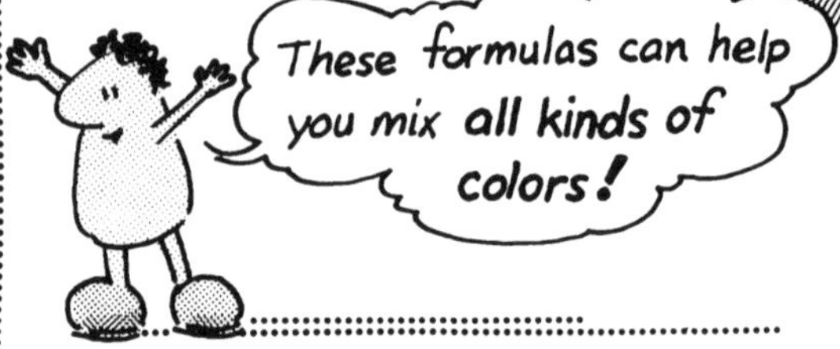

These formulas can help you mix all kinds of colors!

MIXING *THREE* PRIMARIES MAKES BROWN — ______ + ______ + ______ = ______

Objective

To discover how primary colors mix to form secondary colors plus brown. To introduce a foil mini-paint system useful in future painting activities.

Lesson Notes

1-2. Doubling the foil provides enough strength to keep it from tearing as cup impressions are made in step 2.

3. Gather these tempera colors: blue, red and yellow (you will also need white and black for the next activity.) They should be pure, not shades of green, orange or purple. You'll use the 3 primaries in this activity. Most tempera paint is sold as a water soluble powder, though some brands come premixed.

To mix, gather at least 5 containers with airtight lids. If you use quart-sized jars, fill them perhaps 1/5 full with water, then add paint and mix with a plastic straw. After mixing, you can seal each straw inside its jar to use again as a mixing/dispensing tool. Or you can use smaller baby food jars. Smaller containers keep out more air, but you'll have to rinse the straws after each use, instead of sealing them inside the jars.

The intensity of blue and red tempera colors tends to dominate yellow. You can moderate this effect by mixing the yellow to a thicker consistency. Also, adding a few drops of white to the blue and red will make these colors less intense (The blue may require more lightening than the red). You can test the balance by mixing equal amounts of blue and red. This should yield an obvious purple.

All the paints will thicken and dry over time. Just add water and mix vigorously with the straw to return each color to its desired consistency.

If your class is large, double the number of paint jars. In addition, add a few extra jars of yellow to satisfy the greater demand for this color. If you place the jars at several stations around your classroom, you can prevent congestion in any one area.

Only tiny amounts of paint are required in this and subsequent activities. The colors you prepare now should last throughout all painting activities in this module.

To dispense paint, just dip the straw, hold it over a small cup, and let gravity do the rest. Do not use the straw like a pipet, covering the end with your thumb – this will dump too much paint into the tiny foil cups.

4-6. This painting activity cycles through 5 distinct steps:

- ✔ dab paint on the palette with your finger,
- ✔ wipe your finger with a damp towel,
- ✔ dab a different color on your palette,
- ✔ blend the colors into a new color,
- ✔ fingerpaint a color sample in the oval.

While these steps are familiar to anyone with painting experience, they can be confusing to beginners. If your class experiences difficulty, give a mini-demonstration. Emphasize that paint should be mixed on the lid palette, *not* the worksheet oval: that fingertips should be wiped across the damp towel before changing to a new color.

Beware of paper pigs! You only need one towel to do this activity, and another to clean up. Only the very tip of one index finger needs to be dipped in the paint. As the towel becomes saturated, fold painted surfaces to the inside, exposing clean new paper to the outside.

6. Watch out for students who begin this step on the wrong surface. They should mix their colors on the lid palette first, before applying them to each oval.

In the second mix sequence of step 6, if the reds and blues are too intense, their combinations may look more brown than purple (See third paragraph of step 3.) But after 2 dilutions with water (a wet finger will do), the white paper background will allow a truer purple to show through.

Cleanup is real easy. Just throw away the foil paint set and clean the lid. Seal all paint containers tightly so the colors will remain liquid, ready to use in the next activity.

Answers

5-6. Check the color swatches in each oval.

7. blue + yellow = green
   blue + red = purple
   red + yellow = orange
   blue + yellow + red = brown

Materials

☐ Aluminum foil.
☐ Large metal washers, with 1.5 cm (1/2 inch) diameter hole.
☐ Jars of tempera paint in primary colors – red, blue and yellow. See step 3.
☐ Plastic straws for mixing and dispensing paint.
☐ White plastic lids, one per student, to use as paint palettes. Margarine lids are suitable. At least one side should be white (Mixing paint on a colored background makes it difficult to see the paint's true value.) Ask your students to bring lids from home. If you assign each student to bring in two, this easily compensates for those who don't bring any.
☐ Paper towels.
☐ A water source. If running water is not available, use a bucket.

TINTS AND SHADES

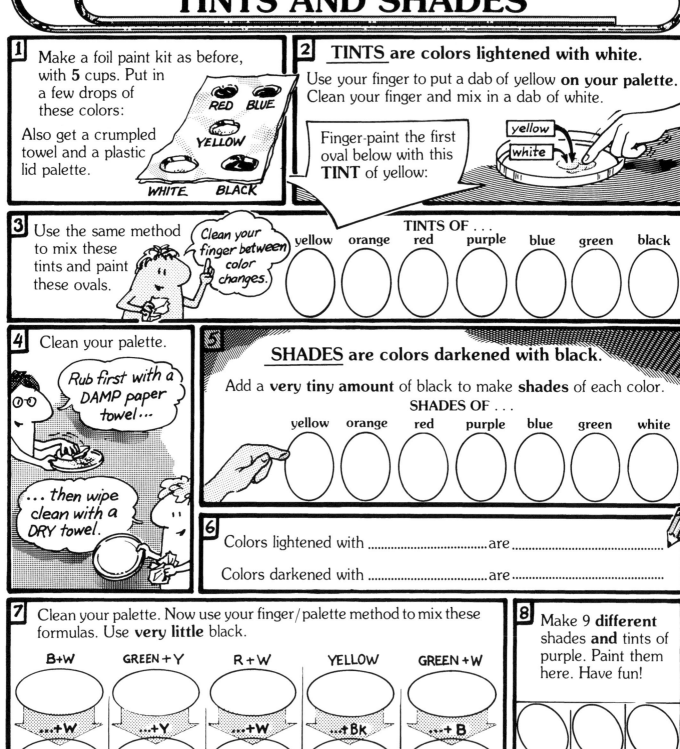

1 Make a foil paint kit as before, with **5** cups. Put in a few drops of these colors:

Also get a crumpled towel and a plastic lid palette.

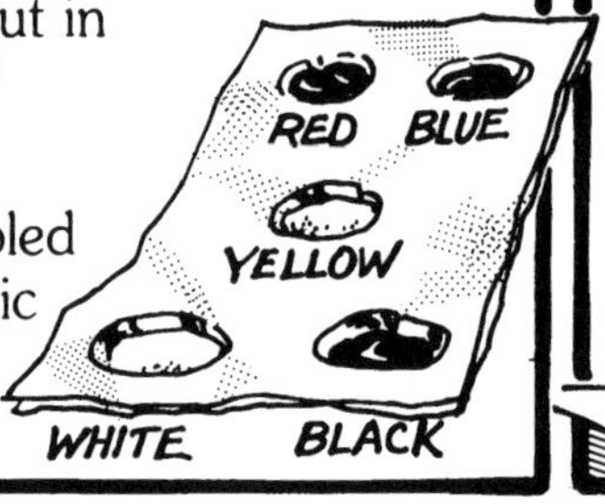

2 **TINTS are colors lightened with white.**

Use your finger to put a dab of yellow **on your palette.** Clean your finger and mix in a dab of white.

Finger-paint the first oval below with this **TINT** of yellow:

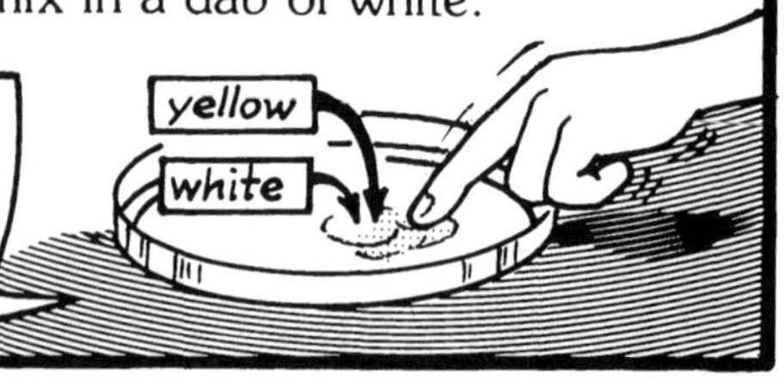

3 Use the same method to mix these tints and paint these ovals.

Clean your finger between color changes.

TINTS OF . . .

yellow	orange	red	purple	blue	green	black

4 Clean your palette.

Rub first with a DAMP paper towel...
... then wipe clean with a DRY towel.

5 **SHADES are colors darkened with black.**

Add a **very tiny amount** of black to make **shades** of each color.

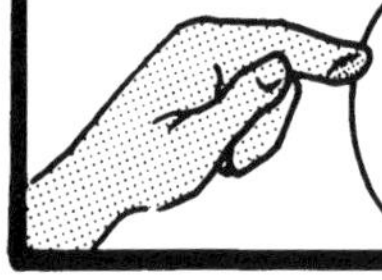

SHADES OF . . .

yellow	orange	red	purple	blue	green	white

6 Colors lightened with .... are ....

Colors darkened with .... are ....

7 Clean your palette. Now use your finger/palette method to mix these formulas. Use **very little** black.

B+W	GREEN + Y	R + W	YELLOW	GREEN + W
...+W	...+Y	...+W	...+Bk	...+ B
...+W	...+Y	...+Y	...+Y	...+Bk

PUZZLE: Circle the oval that is both a tint and a shade!

8 Make 9 **different** shades **and** tints of purple. Paint them here. Have fun!

Objective

To study tinting and shading. To learn how to mix a broader, more subtle spectrum of color.

Lesson Notes

1. This color mixing activity is an expansion of the last. Students make another mini-paint set from foil, just as before. This time 5 washer-hole impressions are pushed into the doubled-over foil. Add black and white to the paint set, in addition to the three primaries.

2. Again, students should first blend colors on their lid palettes, then paint a sample of the resulting tint on each activity sheet oval. Remind them to wipe each color from their finger with a damp paper towel before dipping into a new color.

3. Making tints of primary colors is easy. Simply add white. To make tints of orange, purple or green, students must first recall how to make these secondaries from their primary components. If they forget, they can refer to their previous worksheet.

4. If access to water is limited to only one bucket, this "dry cleaning" technique works well. First rub the lid with a used, paint-soaked towel. Then before the smeared colors dry, wipe with a clean, dry towel.

5. Stress that black is an extremely concentrated color. If your students use more than just a tiny amount, they will produce an uninteresting series of 7 black smudges.

Answers

3, 5, 7, 8. Check the color swatches in each oval.

6. Colors lightened with white are tints.
Colors darkened with black are shades.

7. Puzzle: The oval in the lower right corner contains both W and Bk. It is thus both a tint and a shade.

Materials

- ☐ Aluminum foil.
- ☐ Large metal washers, used in activity 8.
- ☐ Jars of tempera paint - red, blue and yellow, plus black and white. (See teaching notes 8, step 3.)
- ☐ Plastic straws for mixing and dispensing paint.
- ☐ White plastic lids, one per student, to use as paint palettes.
- ☐ Paper towels.
- ☐ A water source, running water or a bucket.

OVER THE RAINBOW

1 Make a foil paint kit with the 3 primary color plus black and white.

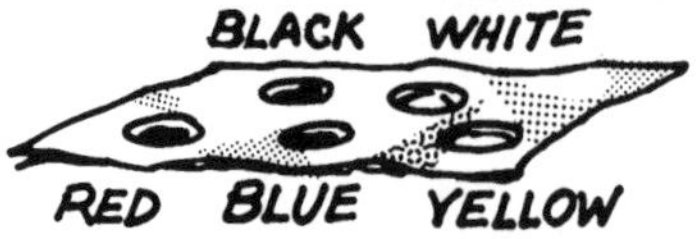

2 Get a palette and a damp paper towel.

3 **FIRST** finger-paint the color on your palette . . . **THEN** finger-paint the oval . . . **THEN** write your color formula.

GREENISH-YELLOW	=	B + Y + Y + Y
ORANGE	=	
BLUE-GREEN	=	
PALE TINT OF RED	=	
MEDIUM SHADE OF BLUE	=	
REDDISH-PURPLE	=	
SKY BLUE TINT	=	
LIGHT BROWN	=	
MATCH THE COLOR OF YOUR PENCIL	=	
MATCH THE COLOR OF YOUR SHOE.	=	

4 Mix up your own mystery color and finger-paint it here.

MYSTERY COLOR

FOLD AND TAPE

Write your formula here.

MYSTERY FORMULA:

5 Ask a friend to match your color and guess your formula:

trial 1 | trial 2 | trial 3

FORMULA:

TOPS LEARNING SYSTEMS

Objective

To practice mixing and blending primary colors, plus white and black, to match any given color value.

Lesson Notes

Is it not strange to encounter three activities about color mixing in the middle of a module about animal survival? Not really. Animals are masters of coloration. Their survival depends on it. The skills your students learn here enable them to create critters later on that can camouflage, mimic, confuse, warn and attract — all by using color.

1-2. By now this coloring system should be familiar to all, Refer newcomers or students in doubt to the expanded directions in activity 8.

3. This step contains a series of 10 puzzles. In each puzzle, a specific color is given. The challenge is to mix and match the primaries, to tint and shade until you blend the given color.

Don't give away any answers. Activity sheets 8 and 9 have provided all the color theory your students need to know. If you insist that your students rise to the occasion, they probably will. Don't be surprised to see real growth — an improved ability to discern color and a more detailed knowledge of how it works.

4. The challenge here is to guess color combinations that are blended by a friend. Color experts in your class may be able to guess the correct formula simply by looking at the test patch. Be aware that 1 in 7 males is red-green color blind to some degree. Certain boys in your class may be physiologically unable to match subtle differences in color, no matter how hard they try.

Answers

3. greenish-yellow = B + Y + Y + Y
orange = R + Y (+ Y)
blue-green = B + Y (+ Y)
pale tint of red = R + W + W (+ W)
medium shade of blue = B + Bk
reddish-purple = B + R + R
sky blue tint = B + W (+ W)
light brown = B + R + Y (+ Y) + W

Materials

☐ A 5-color foil paint set plus accessories (see activity 9).

PAINT THE LANDSCAPE

1 Make a foil paint set using the primary colors plus white.
(Include **2** cups of yellow.)

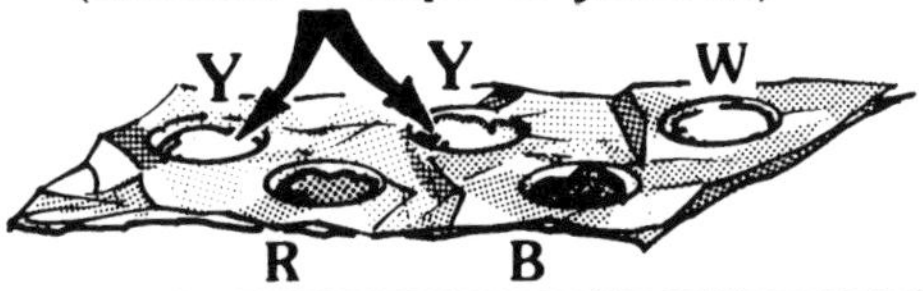

2 Animals wear many colors. Paint each box with the correct color.

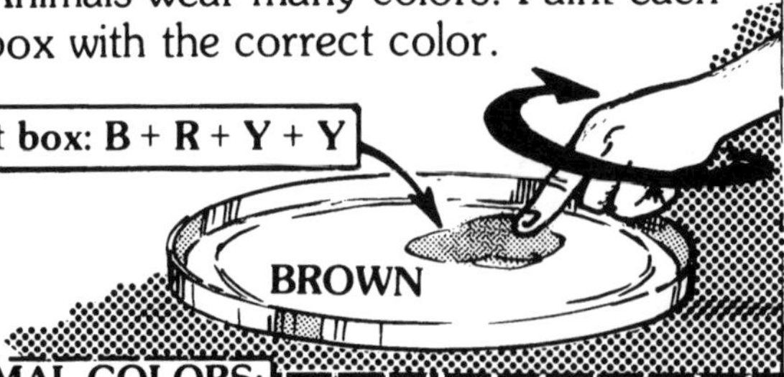

Wipe your finger on a damp paper towel.

ANIMAL COLORS:

B + R + Y + Y	B + Y + Y	B + W	R	Y
Med. BROWN	Med. GREEN	Med. BLUE	RED	YELLOW

3 Animals live in many different places. Paint these animal environments to make them look natural . . . . . . First finger-mix the color you want on your palette . . . . . . then use a brush to paint each pattern below.

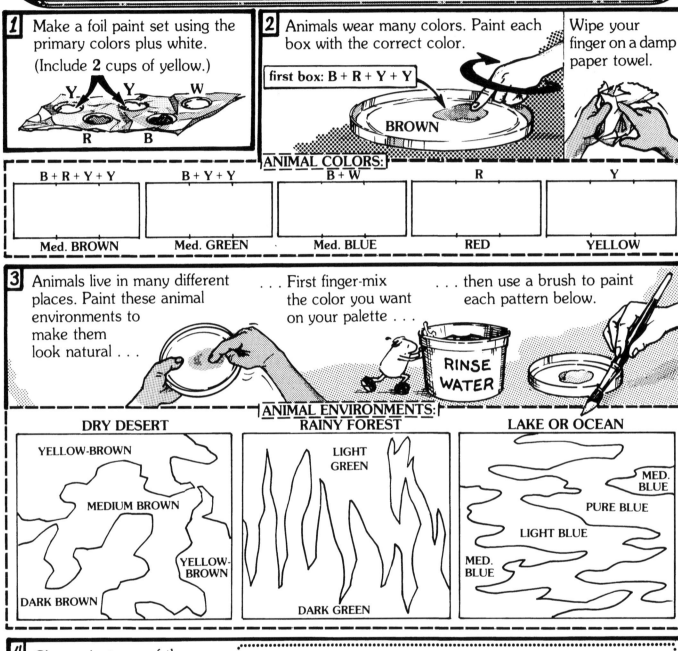

ANIMAL ENVIRONMENTS:

DRY DESERT

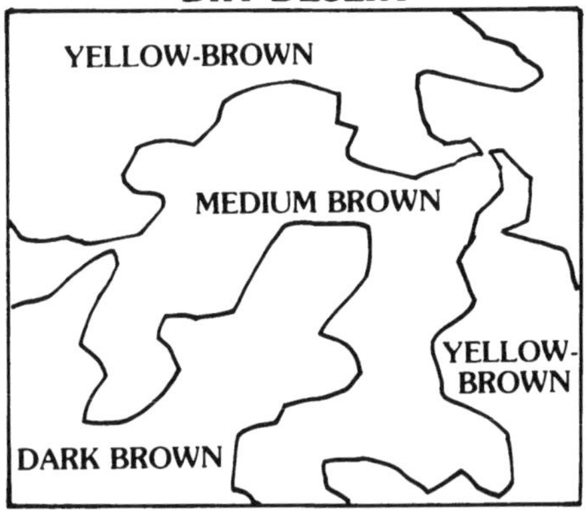

RAINY FOREST

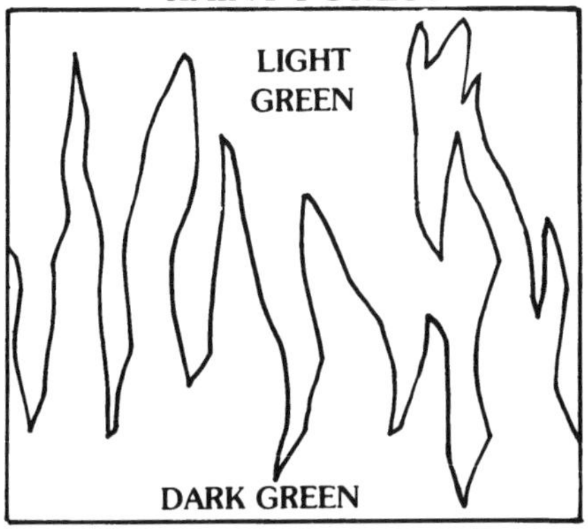

LAKE OR OCEAN

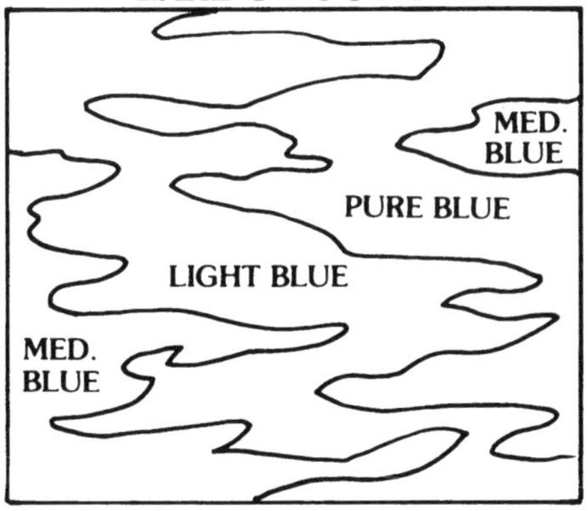

4 Choose just one of the animal environments above.

....
MY CHOICE

First **draw,** then **paint** a critter that can easily survive in this habitat.

Objective

To create 3 natural-looking environments, then paint a critter that can survive in one of them.

Lesson Notes

1. Notice that the foil has 5 paint cups, as usual. But there are only four colors. An extra cup of yellow is needed to lighten the browns and greens. This replaces black, which is not needed at all.

2-3. Formulas for the "animal colors" establish a standard for "medium" shades of brown, green and blue. As you mix the "medium" colors for each animal environment in step 3, try to match them to the corresponding "medium" animal shades in step 2.

In activity 12, these "animal colors" will be cut and pasted into each "animal environment", to test for camouflage properties. For now, they only need to be painted.

3. These environments contain too much detail to be painted with stubby fingers. Only a brush can get into all the nooks and crannies. Students should first finger-mix the correct color on their lid palette, then transfer it to each pattern with a brush, If the blended color dries out on the palette, a moist brush will reliquefy it.

Why finger-mix the paint, when brushes are available? The problem is that brushes hold too much water relative to the tiny amounts of paint in the mini-set. Brush mixing quickly dilutes all the colors to a weak, insipid soup, unless you first dry the brush on a paper towel after each rinse.

4. Though the word "camouflage" has not yet been mentioned, most students will want to create critters that blend with their chosen environment: perhaps a brown desert lizard, a green rain forest frog, or a blue ocean fish. Students instinctively appreciate that survival depends on not being too conspicuous – well, at least some students.

Notice that the friendly TOPS peoplet encourages students to fill up the entire space. Self-conscious artists tend to hide their work by drawing tiny figures. You can increase confidence (and expand drawings) by offering encouragement and sincere praise at every opportunity.

Answers

2. Check the color swatches in each rectangle.

3. Evaluate each colored "environment."

4. Varied drawings.

Materials

☐ Use all paint materials from activity 9, except black tempera paint.
☐ A small container of rinse water.
☐ A paint brush.

OH SAY, CAN YOU SEE?

1 Cut out the animal **COLORS** and **ENVIRONMENTS** from your last worksheet.

2 Cut each **ANIMAL COLOR** into 3 squares of equal size.

3 Tape 5 of these "animal" squares, one of **each color,** into each of the 3 **ENVIRONMENTS.**

4 Look at your "animals" from far away. Order their colors in this table by how easy they are to see:

DRY DESERT	RAINY FOREST	LAKE/OCEAN

5

You are . . .	Choose your best color. Use your results in step 4 to support your hypothesis:	Give a real-life example:
...a desert mammal trying to hide.		
...a swamp amphibian hunting food.		
...a bird trying to attract a mate.		
...an animal living in tall grass that dries out in summer.		
...an insect that can warn that you are dangerous.		
...a fish that lives near the ocean surface.		
...a bird that flies north to summer forests, south to winter lakes.		

Objective

To experimentally determine which colors camouflage best in 3 simulated natural environments. To relate this information to animal coloration.

Lesson Notes

1-3. Your students will cut activity 11 into many pieces as they remove the necessary elements. To help them keep track of the remaining bottom piece, the one with the painted animal, ask them to tape or paste it to a full-sized sheet of paper; then write their name at the top, and put it back in their personal work folder.

Students must further subdivide the 5 painted rectangles into trios of colored squares. Marks on the edges of each rectangle enable them to cut all squares to equal size. Be sure your students tape or glue the squares randomly into the larger environments, not into neat patterns or rows. The whole idea, of course, is for color, not location, to determine which squares are most hidden and which squares are most visible.

4. Students might test their own squares, or better yet, observe the less familiar squares of a friend. Red and yellow will probably place higher on the observation table than blue, green and brown. These last three colors are particularly difficult to see in environments that are painted the same color.

Expect to see minor variations as students rank the colors. Color vision is not uniform, nor are the squares and environments painted with uniform consistency.

5. Accept any hypothesis that is reasonably supported by the previous color observations in step 4. Students who can't seem to make the logical connection might need to think of the colored paper squares as real animals.

It is an oversimplification, of course, to think of marine environments as "blue." An ocean or lake might appear blue one day, then greenish-grey the next, due to changing weather conditions. Hold up a glass of water taken from this same ocean or lake and it appears clear. Other environments are also much more complex than painted in this activity. The overall principle, however, still holds: animals hide by blending, by looking like their environment.

The narrow column at the right asks students to cite a real-life example for each theoretical animal they describe in the middle column. This may or may not be an easy task, depending on each student's personal knowledge of animals. Those who require more background might be sent to the library. Or you can simply suggest a suitable answer.

Answers

4. DRY DESERT	RAINY FOREST	LAKE/OCEAN
blue	red	yellow
red	yellow	red
yellow	blue	brown
green	brown	green
brown	green	blue

5. ...desert mammal: Brown like a mouse. This color square was hardest to see on a dry desert background.

...swamp amphibian: Green like a frog. This color square was hardest to see on a rainy forest background.

...an attracting bird: Red (or yellow) like a robin (or canary). These colors were relatively easy to see in all of the environments.

...animal in tall grass: Green changing to brown like a lizard. As the grass changes color, so does the camouflage.

...a warning insect: Yellow (or red) like a bee (or lady bug). These are easy-to-see colors in all environments.

...an ocean fish: Blue like a swordfish. This colored square was hardest to see in a lake or ocean environment.

...a migrating bird: Green changing to blue, like some ducks. These colors provide camouflage in summer forests and winter lakes.

Extension

Toss a handful of toothpicks of different colors into a grassy area outside. Run a *double* relay race (each runner cycles through twice). Each player must run to the grassy area, pick up the first visible toothpick (one only each time!), run back to drop it in a "found box", then tag the next person in line.

Tally the total number of toothpicks found for each color Discuss how the toothpicks might represent real animals. Repeat this activity on a dusty field. Predict how the numbers should change, then verify.

Here is how to organize this activity:

1. Divide your class into 3 equal teams (Odd students out can be judges.) Choose names for each team – owls, wolves, bobcats, etc.

2. Use 5 different colors of toothpicks, red, blue, yellow, green and natural (or brown). Or substitute strips of colored paper.

3. Multiply your class size by 0.6, rounding off to the nearest whole number. Use this number of toothpicks for each color (Total toothpicks equal 5 times this many.) This will leave about a third of the toothpicks remaining after the relay race.

Materials

☐ Activity sheet 11, fully painted.
☐ Scissors.
☐ Cellophane tape or glue.

NOW YOU SEE IT

1 Cut out 1 square at the bottom of this page.

2 Choose a resting place for this moth that you can easily see from the center of the room . . .

. . . carefully paint your moth to look exactly like its resting place.

3 Cut out your moth and write your name on the back.

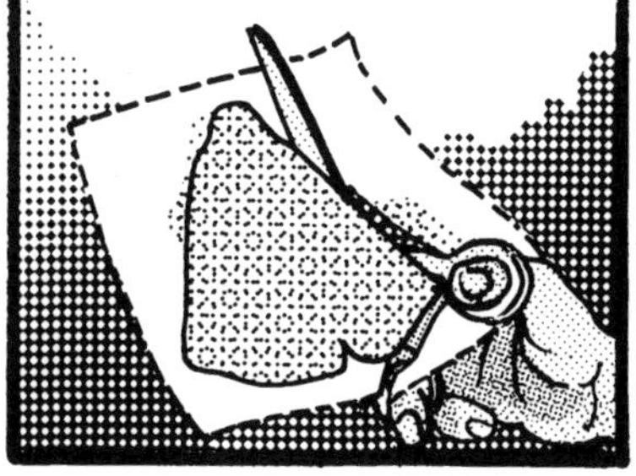

4 Fix your moth to its resting place with a small piece of tape rolled sticky-side out.

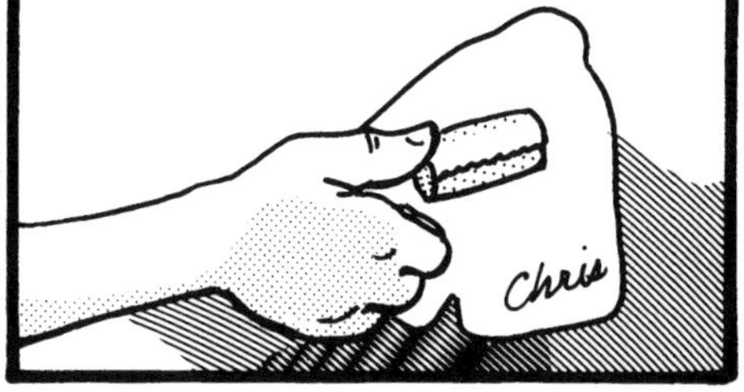

5 Keep track of time. Moths must be in place before the birds come!

6 Which kind of animal needs to use camouflage: the hunter, the hunted, or both? Explain.

. . . continue on back . . .

7 List advantages and problems of using camouflage.

ADVANTAGES	PROBLEMS

. . . continue on back . . .

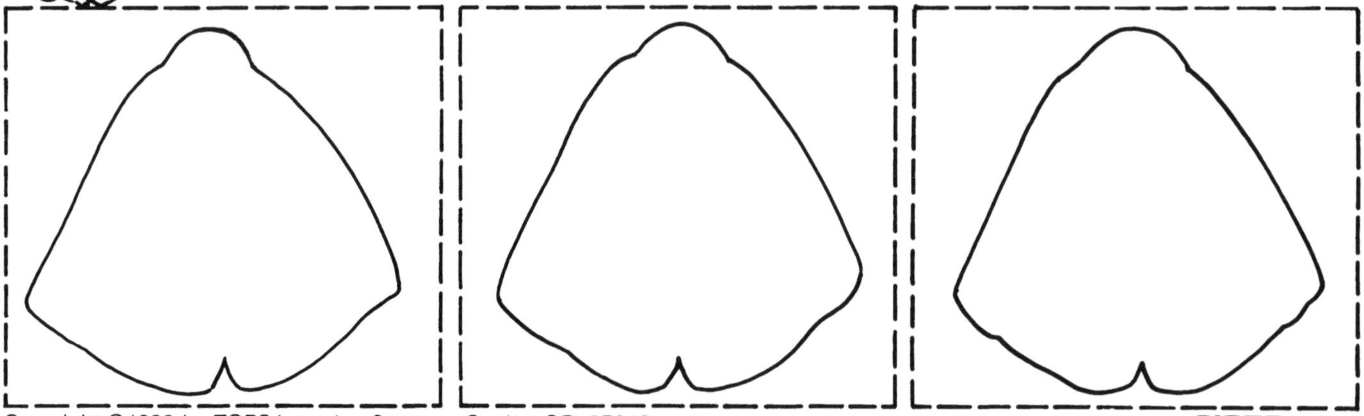

Objective

To camouflage paper moths so they blend into the patterns and textures of classroom surfaces.

Lesson Notes

Careful, thoughtful work requires lots of time. Students may need a whole period to create just one well-camouflaged moth (steps 1-5), to be visited by the birds (between steps 5 and 6) and to debrief (steps 6-7). If this is all the time you can afford to spend, it is better to limit your students to one moth done well than 3 moths done poorly.

Students can, of course make several attempts, then expose their best moth to the scrutiny of the birds. If possible, spend an entire class period camouflaging all three moths well. Then arrange to have the birds come on another day.

1-3. Notice that the entire square is cut out and painted before the moth shape itself is trimmed in step 3. This allows paint that extends beyond the moth outline to be trimmed away, and both furniture and walls remain clean. Suggest that students cut just *inside* the black line. A well camouflaged moth doesn't show its outline.

2. Pick resting sights with great care. The survival of your moth depends on it! Stress these ground rules: The moths must be plainly visible from the center of the room, not resting under or behind things or otherwise out of view. They must be within easy reach, not taped to a 10 foot ceiling or fixed to the outside of a window.

To match colors and textures, students need the freedom to stand close to the surface they wish to duplicate. Encourage them to test color blends on pieces of scratch paper before painting their moths. Keep extra moth patterns available for those who mess up.

5. "The birds are coming! The birds are coming! Get ready for the birds!" As the time approaches, you can generate great anticipation and excitement. Students may question if the birds are real. Be vague and cagey about your answer. Of course they are real, alive and breathing!

Students need to manage their time well. Let them know when the birds will arrive. Stay on schedule. It the moths aren't ready, too bad.

Here is a wonderful opportunity to introduce other faculty, even the school principal, to the wonders of hands-on science. Prearrange to have a group of 3 or 4 "birds," students and/or adults, scratch on your door at the appointed hour. Show them a moth pattern in advance so they know what they're looking for. Tell them that these moths will be in plain view about your room, but difficult to see.

When you open the door, the birds should swoop into your room and snatch up as many moths as they can find before you shout "TIME." Each time they find one, they should remove it from its resting place and shout "MEAL TIME" or some such phrase.

Determine how many moths are in place before the birds arrive. Count the number of times you hear "MEAL TIME" during the hunt, so you can call "TIME" before all the moths are eaten. Allow at least 10% of the moths to "survive," perhaps more it they are well camouflaged.

6-7. Shoo away the birds as quickly as they came. Make sure they leave all "prey" on a designated desk top. Discuss why some moths survived and others didn't. Are luck and location important factors? Discuss the concepts, reserving enough time for students to thoughtfully answer each question. You may wish to honor the survivors in a special bulletin board display.

Answers

6. Both the hunter and the hunted need camouflage. The lion, owl or spider need to surprise their prey. The antelope, field mouse and moth need to escape being noticed.

7. ADVANTAGES: Camouflage is easy to use. Just keep still. More elaborate forms of protection, like speed, protective covering, or poison are not needed.

PROBLEMS: Camouflage doesn't work as well when moving. Nor will it work equally well in all environments, in a green spring meadow, for example, compared to a snowy winter meadow.

Materials

- ☐ A foil paint set plus accessories. See activity 9 for a complete listing.
- ☐ A paint brush plus rinse water.
- ☐ Scissors.
- ☐ Tape.

IT'S ALL IN YOUR MIME

It was a typical summer morning, the smell of wilting heat returning after the cool safe night. With the sun would come the danger. The class restlessly hung at attention in the deep notch of the massive maple tree. Today would bring the long-awaited field trip, and the sound of anxious feet began to annoy the teacher.

"Keep your feet still, all six of them." Carefully she repeated the lesson of the past week for the last time. Attention returned to the class, except for the regular disruptors, Leroy and Chuck. It seemed that Leroy suffered from a strange illness, which forced him to laugh at every dumb sound that exploded from old Chuckie's tireless mouth.

"Mimicry, that's the secret. If you forget, well — just don't forget. Remember, mimicry means hiding by looking like something inedible. Camouflage is easy; you just try to match your background, so your enemy doesn't notice you. We, however, stand out where we can be seen, but not recognized. If we're on a leaf, we spread out to look like veins. If we're on a twig, we pull together and become another twig. Hiding is so common. Mimicry is our way, the best way."

The time had come. The small class of walking sticks scrambled out of the safe, dark area. This would be their first time out on the end of the branch. It was glorious! Just like the grownups.

Suddenly, the sky grew dark, and the hearts of the little bugs were filled with terror. Slowly control returned to the well-trained group. "Remember." And they did. Small groups of leaf veins and twigs, not an insect to be seen!

The shadow grew larger, until two legs, then a body, and finally the savage head appeared. The bird paused, searched, found nothing, then prepared to depart, unfed. Not quite. You see, good old Chuck needed to make a sound, any sound. Leroy added his customary laugh, and the rest is history.

The next day at the funeral, no bodies being present, the "words" were repeated. "Mimicry works if you stand completely, perfectly still — and nobody bugs you."

1 Make a paper cornflake that looks like a real cornflake.

2 Fold 4 index cards in half the short way.

3 Glue your cornflake **mimic** on one card, and 3 **real** cornflakes on the others.

4 Mix up the cards while a friend stands far away.

5 Find out how close your friend can get and still **not** see your mimic.

6 Measure the **MINIMUM SAFE DISTANCE**: Use this ruler and some string.

Objective

To understand mimicry as a survival strategy. To cleverly mimic the appearance of a corn flake.

Lesson Notes

Mimics survive by looking like something else: the tortoise resembles a rock; the katydid looks like a leaf: the viceroy butterfly (a sweet bird treat) mimics the poisonous monarch.

To mimic is to copy some object in particular. A walking stick mimics a twig by actually looking like a twig in every respect. To camouflage, by contrast, is to deceive in a more generalized way. A free moth uses camouflage to blend in with many surfaces in general, but no object in particular.

Chuck and Leroy were unsuccessful mimics. Their story is instructive; read it with your class. After the story, discuss mimicry as a copycat strategy to look like something else. Compare and contrast mimicry to camouflage.

You may want students to add a page or so to this story, creating new characters and adventures. To encourage growth and intellectual development, introduce writing and language skills into your curriculum as often as possible.

1. By now your class has enough color blending experience to create great mimics. Mixing the perfect shade of orange, imitating shape and size, and matching the exact texture all involve a heady mix of high order thought processes. The use of judgement, verification, evaluation and self-correction all come into play.

Students who create poor imitations are continuing to operate with lower order skills, refusing to stay on task until the job is done right. Your examples can make a big difference. Work right along with your class. Let them see you concentrate, struggle, and rework until you create a perfect imitation.

2-4. Having created the best possible artificial flake, now choose real corn flakes to mimic the mimic! Select ones that have similar size and shape. Glue them on identical index cards in similar positions. This will minimize contextual clues Even though others have seen you make your fake flake and glue it to an index card, when all 4 cards are shuffled, everything will look the same. The mimic won't stand out as being larger or smaller, or resting higher or lower than the rest.

5. No mimic can stand up to very close scrutiny, not even a walking stick. The idea here is to move slowly forward from the back of the room until you can recognize your mimic (or someone else's) with certainty. Take a step or two back, and you have established a minimum safe distance. Use the worksheet ruler to express the distance in meters.

If time permits, create a panel of judges to select the 4 best mimics. While your students are out of the room, line up these mimics on the chalk tray of your blackboard along with 12 authentic corn flakes. Number all 12 positions on the board.

Ask your class to stand away from the blackboard, on the opposite side of the room. Call out each numbered position, asking students to raise their hands each time they think you have selected one of the four mimics. Find the fake flake that drew the fewest votes (fooled the most students). Honor its creator as the class mimic champion.

Extension

Create an art collage of simple materials. One of the objects in your collage must be an imitation. Can you compose the collage so cleverly that a casual observer will not notice the mimic?

Answers

6. Students should report the minimum safe distance of their mimic in meters.

Materials

- ☐ A 5 color foil paint set plus accessories.
- ☐ Glue.
- ☐ A paint brush plus water rinse.
- ☐ 3x5 index cards – 4 for each student.
- ☐ Scissors.
- ☐ Corn flakes.
- ☐ String. Or substitute a meter tape.

ATTENTION PLEASE!

1 Identify these signs:

COLORS:					
MESSAGE:					

2 Design 3 eye-catching signs. Think about **shape, message** and **color.**

Advertise something:	Issue a warning:	Pass on important information:

3 Animals advertise themselves just like signs.

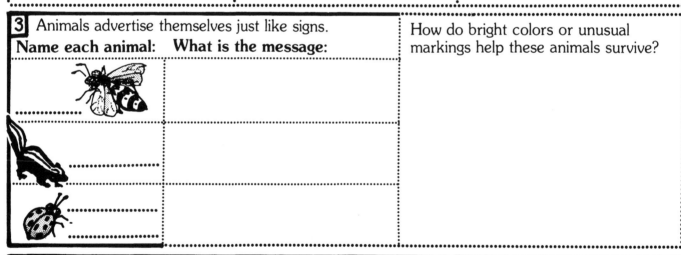

Name each animal:	**What is the message:**

How do bright colors or unusual markings help these animals survive?

4 Invent some **warning colors** and **patterns** for these skin patches.

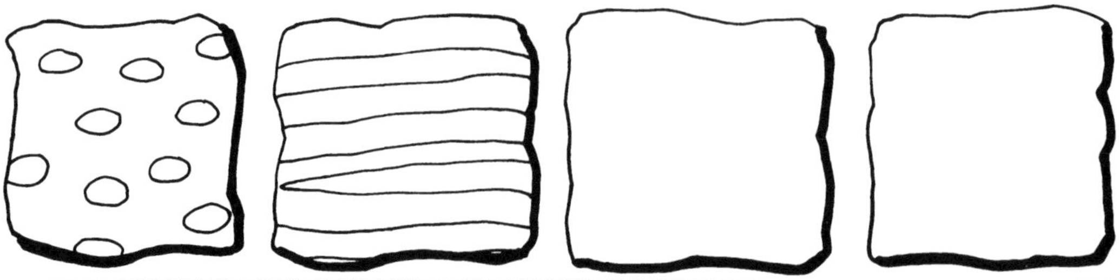

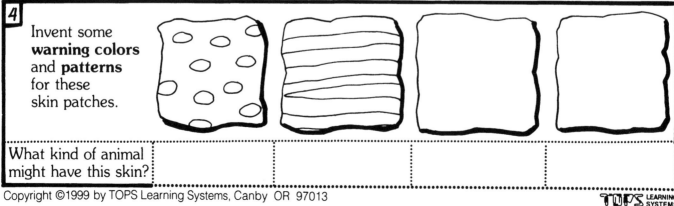

What kind of animal might have this skin?				

TOPS LEARNING SYSTEMS

Objective

To understand how animals use shape, color and sound to warn away predators.

Lesson Notes

1. Traffic signs deliver messages on three distinct levels. A stop sign, for example, sends its all important message as a specific shape (octagon), a characteristic color (red), and written message (STOP).

Animals use these same forms of communication. A snake might warn by coiling into a specific shape; by displaying an easily recognized pattern of color; by hissing a warning message.

2. Encourage students to "design" in the true sense of the word: to think carefully before responding. Good designers use higher-order thought processes. They consider different options, organize ideas, formulate plans and execute them thoughtfully.

Motivate with encouragement and praise. Show students what is possible by example. At least some will live up to your expectations. So expect the best.

Discussion

Reinforce the main ideas in this activity with a class discussion that covers the following:

Black and yellow stripes, by themselves, don't communicate anything at all. A naive animal, for example, might even be attracted to a bright wonderful pattern the first time. Once stung, however, the victim learns to associate colorful stripes with pain. Yellow and black take on a new meaning! (In the same manner, a red octagon takes on new meaning to a driver that is ticketed for running a stop sign.)

Learned associations tend to become generalized. Once stung by a bee, an animal will certainly avoid not only bees but wasps and hornets as well. All brightly colored animals may be approached with somewhat greater caution.

The skunk is nocturnal, a night feeder. If it were colored completely black, this superior camouflage would make it much harder to see. But smell and camouflage are incompatible defenses. If a skunk's enemies cannot see it clearly enough to instantly recognize its warning, it could be attacked and injured or killed, although the hunter would be left with a terrible smell about it.

Many kinds of insects, amphibians, reptiles, and fish advertise with bright colors and patterns that they are poisonous or taste bad. These animals make wonderful subjects for other nonoffensive animals to mimic. The viceroy butterfly, for example, mimics the poisonous monarch, even though it has no poison of its own. The harmless king snake mimics the deadly poisonous coral snake, scaring off predators with pure deception.

During the course of your discussion someone may mention zebras. Zebras do not warn, yet they wear distinctive patterns. Within the context of a stampeding herd, stripes give the animals another kind of advantage: the rapidly changing patterns break up specific body outlines, making individual animals harder to select and hunt down.

Answers

1.

STOP SIGN	TRAFFIC LIGHT	SKULL
red/white	green	white/black
stop	go	poison

NO SMOKING	RR CROSSING
red/white/black	white/black
no smoking	RR crossing

2. Students should design and draw 3 original signs.

3. BEE: Leave me alone or I'll sting you.
SKUNK: Stay away. I smell bad.
LADY BUG: Don't eat me. I taste bad.

The bright colors or unusual markings warn that these animals are "trouble" before the predator decides to attack. The brighter or more unusual, the better. *After* is too late.

4. Students should complete 4 patterns and corresponding animals.

Materials

☐ A 5-color foil paint set plus accessories (Color blending is not significant in this activity. Substitute crayons or colored pencils if you wish.)

SOUND OFF

1 List 2 examples of people or machines that make each of these sounds:

SOUND:	WHAT MAKES IT?	WHAT'S THE MESSAGE?
Ringing	1 *Telephone*	*Someone wants to talk with you.*
	2	
Siren	1	
	2	
Horn	1	
	2	
Alarm	1	
	2	
Whistle	1	
	2	

2 What is each animal saying? Write your best guess in each bubble.

3 Record warning or information sounds around your home or neighborhood. Try to include unusual sounds that no one will know.

If you **can** borrow a tape recorder . . .
Put actual sounds on tape, and say what each means. Leave about 5 seconds of silence after each presentation. (Push "record" with the volume off.)

If you **can't** borrow a tape recorder . . .
Describe the sounds on another paper and write what they mean. Be prepared to imitate one of your sounds (a bird call, for example) in front of the class.

Objective

To understand how animals communicate using sound.

Lesson Notes

Other animals don't share our facility for language. But they do communicate, like us, in nonverbal ways. Animals, like us, are masters of tone, inflection, and gesture. This activity is an invitation to stop and listen to the animals and hear what they say.

1. So many machines now warn us or demand our attention. Watches, dryers, microwaves, seat belts, trucks backing up – the level of auditory stimulation can become so intense, or so routine, that normal signals go unnoticed.

2. Each dialogue bubble should contain a specific message. The dog, for example, should say more than just "bark" or "I'm mad."

3. Stress that any sound is OK to record, as long as it warns or communicates in some manner. For example, a car's horn conveys an intended communication, whereas its engine probably does not. (Some drivers do, however, communicate by revving their engines.)

Those who don't have access to a tape recorder should describe their sounds in writing, then attempt to imitate at least one mystery sound for the class to guess. This may not be easy for your particular age group. Students who explode into fits of embarrassed giggles may not be misbehaving, though it could evolve into that. Give anyone who lacks the requisite self control an out: make these performances optional.

Discussion

We hear thousands of sounds each day. Many go unnoticed due to sensory overload and environmental stress. TV, radio, and a myriad of other less obvious distractions so surround us, that we walk through our world usually reacting to only the most outrageous stimuli.

Discuss the effects of environmental noise pollution and visual over-stimulation. Can you listen to 100 TV commercials in a single day and still maintain your sanity? How does it feel to ride through the city and see endless billboards and signs float by? How does over-stimulation affect your brain, your outlook on life?

Extension

Birds often mark territory with sound. Day after day they visit the same location, at the same time of day, to sing the same song. Try to find an example of this behavior near your home. Record your observations in a journal, or write a report. Make recordings of the bird song on several consecutive days.

Answers

1. Sample answers:

RINGING

Telephone: Someone wants to talk with you.
School Bell: Time to begin a new period; end of an old one.

SIREN

Police Car Siren: Pull over and stop.
Fire Engine Siren: Get out of my way.

HORN

Car Horn: Watch out; hurry up; get moving; I'm here...
Fog Horn: Watch out. Dangerous rocks here.

ALARM

Smoke Detector: There is fire danger.
Burglar Alarm: A robbery is happening.

WHISTLE

Referee's Whistle: Out of bounds; begin play; time out...
Human Whistle: Hey baby! Here dog!

2. SNAKE: Stay away or I'll bite.
   DOG: Get off my turf.
   CRICKET: I'm looking for a mate.
   MONKEY: I'm the leader around here.
   SONG BIRD: This is my territory.
   BEAVER: Watch out. Danger is near.
   WOLF: Hello. Who is out there?
   CAT: Come closer and I'll scratch you.

3. Varied responses.

Materials

☐ A cassette tape recorder. If you provide a standard cassette recorder for class use, students will not have to bring their own recorders to school unless they've used odd-sized tapes.

THE UNTOUCHABLES

1

Name an animal that is covered this way:	How does this covering help the animal survive?	How does each covering also make life more difficult? Explain.	Draw some things people might **use** or **wear** to protect themselves this way.
SHELL: 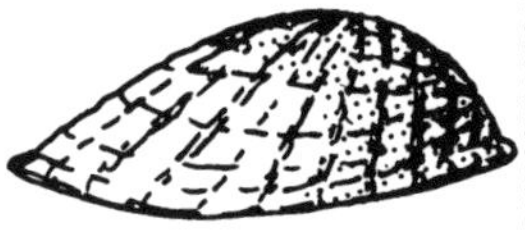 .... ANIMAL?			
ARMOR PLATES:  .... ANIMAL?			
SPINES OR QUILLS: 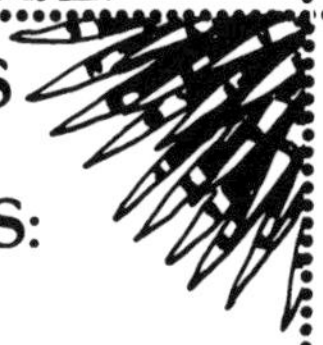 .... ANIMAL?			
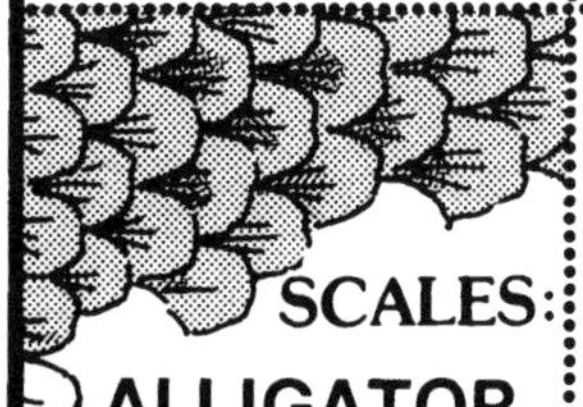 **SCALES:** ALLIGATOR .... ANIMAL?			

2

CHALLENGE:

Can you protect a **hard boiled egg** so well that it won't crack when dropped to a hard floor from a height of 2½ meters?

RULES:

- ☐ Do this activity at home with your own hard-boiled egg.
- ☐ Family members may help, if you wish.
- ☐ Use materials approved by your family. **Egg coverings will be judged on originality** as well as survivability!
- ☐ At least a **square centimeter** of the egg must show in at least **2 different places.** ⟶ 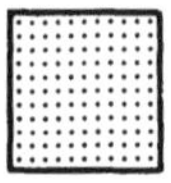
- ☐ On the back of this sheet, draw in detail how you protected your egg.
- ☐ Bring **this sheet** and your **protected egg** to school for testing on ________.

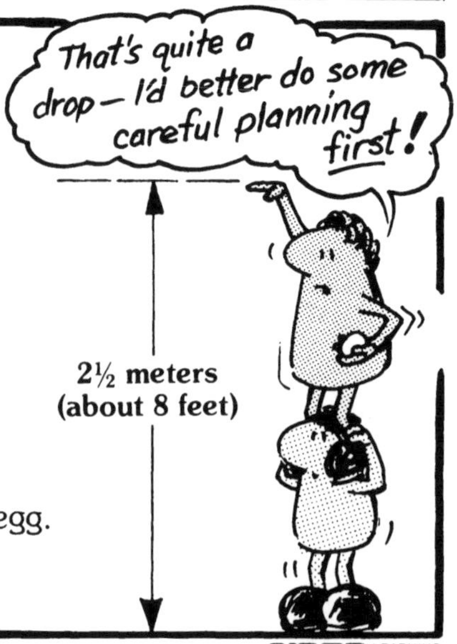
That's quite a drop – I'd better do some careful planning first!
2½ meters
(about 8 feet)

TOPS LEARNING SYSTEMS

Objective

To study variations in protective coverings. To understand that adaptations have disadvantages as well as advantages.

Lesson Notes

1. 1st column: Anyone who has seen wildlife programs on TV or has been to a zoo should be able to think of at least one animal for each category. To stimulate thinking, students might pair up and brainstorm this problem together.

Animals that are probably most familiar to your class are listed in the answer key under each category. There are, of course, many possibilities. Encourage your students to think beyond the commonplace.

SHELLS: clam, crab, mussel, snail, beetle, squid (internal).
ARMOR PLATES: armadillo, sow bug (roley poley), lobster.
SPINES/QUILLS: sea urchin, hedgehog, scorpion fish.
SCALES: alligator, snake, lizard.

2nd column: Students write advantages in this column and disadvantages in the next. Look for complete thoughts, written in complete sentences.

3rd column: Any change for the better usually makes matters worse in some other area. This idea of trade-offs is an important ecological concept that you may want to work into a closing discussion.

4th column: Students will have to exercise their brains to come up with some good examples. Again, encourage students to brainstorm together.

2. This egg challenge is a wonderful way to involve parents and their children in a cooperative problem-solving activity. Before you send this paper home, make sure students record the due date in the blank space provided. This will give parents full information, and make students responsible for turning in their eggs on time.

A number of eggs should survive the drop test. How will you choose the best egg protection from among the survivors?

You could drop them from greater and greater heights. But before you do this, if at all, select the best egg protection based on creativity and originality. Students should appreciate that an egg that comes wrapped in layers and layers of newspaper and tape or a wad of team rubber is not as creatively packaged as an egg that is...

Discussion

Every coin has two sides, so the saying goes. The car gives us rapid mobility..., but smog and expensive road repair as well. TV provides instant information about the world..., but we waste precious time passively watching life go by. These activity sheets are wonderful..., but the paper used to make them quickens the depletion of forested land. Discuss these and other trade-offs.

Answers

1. Sample answers:

SHELL:
Turtle. Predators can't get past the shell to enjoy the meat inside. But a shell is bulky, heavy, and inflexible, making movement slow and difficult.

ARMOR PLATES:
Rhinoceros. Armor plates are too tough to penetrate with teeth and claws. But, the armor requires a lot of extra energy to haul around.

SPINES OR QUILLS:
Porcupine. Predators can't attack without suffering pain and injury. But, quills make it difficult to approach friends as well as foes.

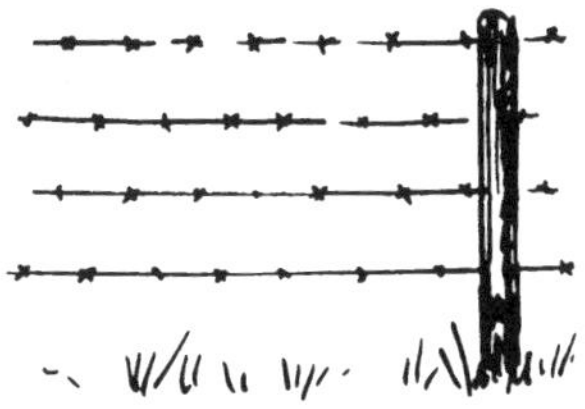

SCALES:
Alligator. Scales are too tough to chew or claw through. But the animal is hunted for its tough, valuable hide.

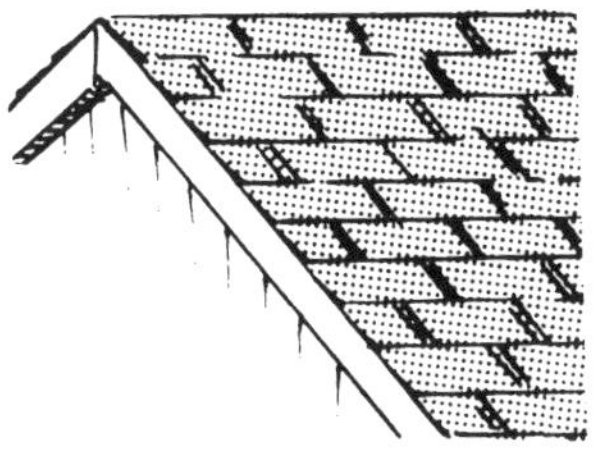

Materials

None for the classroom. Students will use hard-boiled eggs plus basic protection materials from home.

TO RUN OR NOT TO RUN

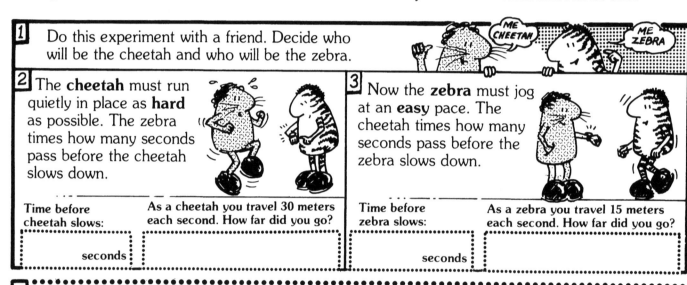

Ask most red-blooded kids to name the fastest land animal in the world, and quickly they answer, "Huh?"

Of course *you* know the answer, the cheetah. Here are some well known facts about this remarkable animal. You already know it can run over 70 miles per hour. But how far does it have to run to get going top speed? Well, if you raced a modern dragster (a super-fast, short-distance race car that can top 200 mph) against a cheetah from one side of this room to the other, the cat would win. You knew the cheetah was a cat, didn't you? Good. This creature can go from 0 to 70 mph in about 5 steps.

Now you'd think that anytime the cheetah was hungry, it would just run out and grab a bite. WRONG! He'd have to race slower animals that can jump, dodge and confuse by running into bushes or herds of other critters.

Well, surely he would eventually catch and kill something, because he could keep the chase going. Nope. This cat, with its fabulous flexible skeleton and magnificent muscles, can run only for the length of time it takes for one breath. The race is over when it has to take a second breath. The fastest land animal catches a meal only about once in seven tries. Not too swift.

1 Do this experiment with a friend. Decide who will be the cheetah and who will be the zebra.

ME CHEETAH
ME ZEBRA

2 The **cheetah** must run quietly in place as **hard** as possible. The zebra times how many seconds pass before the cheetah slows down.

Time before cheetah slows:	As a cheetah you travel 30 meters each second. How far did you go?
seconds	

3 Now the **zebra** must jog at an **easy** pace. The cheetah times how many seconds pass before the zebra slows down.

Time before zebra slows:	As a zebra you travel 15 meters each second. How far did you go?
seconds	

4 Who ran further, the cheetah or the zebra? Explain.

5 You are a rabbit that survives by using camouflage.

Have a friend time how long you can remain **perfectly still.** Get comfortable and signal when to start:

Timing stops at the **first movement** of any kind. Blinking and breathing are OK, but not smiling, shifting, scratching, etc.

YOUR TIME:

trial 1	trial 2

FRIEND'S TIME:

trial 1	trial 2

Find a **CLASS CHAMPION:**

6 Would you rather be a cheetah, a zebra or a rabbit? Write a story about who you are and how you survive.

Write on the back of this sheet.

Objective

To understand speed, endurance, and camouflage as survival techniques. To consider the trade-offs.

Lesson Notes

These activities are very physical, great fun. Your students will run flat out like a cheetah, gallop along like a zebra, or sit perfectly still like a rabbit. To control youthful exuberance you'll need to assume a serious, no-nonsense demeanor.

1-4. Before students begin this activity, emphasize the differences between animal running styles. Cheetahs run hard, flat out, holding nothing back. (Ask a volunteer to demonstrate by running furiously in place for perhaps 5 seconds.) A zebra, however, runs slow and steady. (Ask the same volunteer to run easily in place for another 5 seconds.)

If students adopt these running styles during the experiment. Cheetahs will slow down dramatically and show obvious signs of fatigue within 1 minute. Zebras, however, should be able to run easily for the full five minutes without showing visible fatigue.

It students don't adopt the correct running styles, it is possible that a cheetah will occasionally win (run at least half as long as the zebra). That's OK too. The cheetah, after all, catches something to eat about once in seven tries.

All running times are expressed as seconds, not minutes. Students typically forget to make this conversion, especially when measuring the longer zebra running time.

5. Remaining perfectly still is not easy, especially when you're only a laugh or smile away from having time called on you. That's why each student has 2 chances (trials). Champion rabbit honors will likely go to the best poker face.

6. Students must first identify with their animals of choice, then write a story about how they survive. Encourage them to integrate the main ideas from this activity sheet into the fabric of their story. Their response can be just a few paragraphs long. Or you can assign the story as homework, requiring creative expression that lasts several pages.

Discussion

If cats use bursts of speed to catch prey, how do dogs catch prey? (They run slowly and steadily until they wear the hunted animal down.)

Bears can run and swim much faster than humans. Large ones can reach twelve feet into a tree. If you were attacked by a grizzly bear (and could keep your wits about you), would you use speed, endurance, or stillness to survive?

When confronted by people who threaten you, how would you survive? Would you run? Would you verbally or physically return their aggression? Would you use stillness or passiveness to still their anger and violence?

Answers

2-3. Typical response:
Time before cheetah slows = 60 sec (or 1 minute)
Distance traveled = 60 sec x 30 m/sec = 900 meters
Time before zebra slows = 300 sec (or 5 minutes)
Distance traveled = 300 sec x 15 m/sec = 4,500 meters

4. The zebra ran farther. Even though it ran only half as fast as the cheetah, it ran more than twice as long without tiring.

5. Students should record time in seconds.

6. Accept all thoughtful answers.

Materials

☐ A watch or wall clock that measures seconds.

GET IT TOGETHER

1 Pick a **HABITAT** and glue or tape it here.

Glue or tape a **SURVIVAL STRATEGY** here.

This is WHERE I'll live...
... and this is HOW I'll survive.

2 Design an original (never seen before) creature that fits these two conditions.

MY PLAN		If my creature were real it would...
Head (eyes, mouth)	Limbs (arms and legs)	... be how long? ....
		... be how tall? ....
		... get food by ....
Defenses	Food-getting parts	... be these colors ....
Skin	Other important details	... protect itself by ....
		☐ **Teacher Check**

3 Construct a model of your new creature using odds and ends, construction paper, glue, tape and paint. Make it follow your plans closely.

Make it WONDERFUL!

4 Get ready to give a report about your creation to your class.

I can survive living in .... by ....

Objective

To design fantasy animals that survive by natural means. To review the major survival strategies presented in this book.

Lesson Notes

If students feel the freedom and protection to let their imaginations run wild, you can get multilayered, incredibly complex results from this activity. Stress excellence of thought, design and production.

1. To begin, duplicate enough Selection Squares so that each students gets a white *habitat* square and a black *survival strategy* square. One sheet will accommodate up to 15 students, two sheets up to 30 students.

If your class has 25 members, for example, make 2 copies. Cut out 25 black squares to put in one container (box, can, hat, etc.); put 25 white squares in another. To include as much variation as possible, use all 15 squares in one sheet before you start cutting up the second. Cut out the 10 remaining squares from the second sheet so that all 5 black survival strategy squares are evenly represented with 2 from each category.

Pass the "habitat" container first. Without looking, each student should draw one white square, then paste or tape it into the space provided. Once students know their animal's habitat, ask them to select a black "survival strategy" square in the same manner.

2. These planning boxes are extremely important. They prevent students from rushing carelessly into the construction phase of their project without first thinking through their overall design. Encourage students to express their ideas both graphically and verbally in these boxes, and on the back of the page, if needed.

Require each plan to pass a teacher-check inspection before you allow any cutting or pasting. Evaluate according to these criteria:

• Has the student spent adequate time and energy, commensurate with ability?

• Is the proposed creation of original design? (No natural animals, please!)

• How, specifically, is the animal equipped to survive in its assigned habitat? (If for example, it lives in a dry, dusty place, how does it conserve water? If it survives using camouflage, can it blend into a dry environment? If it is a mimic, does it mimic something commonly found in the desert?)

If necessary, ask students to rework their ideas and come back again for another teacher-check inspection.

3. If materials are available, make the models three dimensional, self supporting, and viewable from any side. Encourage neatness: living things, after all, are not put together in a sloppy fashion. Demand excellence: provide firm direction and motivate with praise. Some students may create model beasts that will astound you in their design, originality, and quality of production.

4-5. Students should prepare well for these oral reports, presenting thoughtful explanations of how their creatures survive. Encourage whole ideas, not one word, dull nothings. Wild flights of fantasy are OK as long as they are intelligently presented. Ask probing questions to expose gaps of thought. Demand that loose ends be tied up.

If a beast is designed well enough to survive in the appointed place and by the strategy selected, it should be elected (by class vote) to the rank of survivor, perhaps placed under a sign labeled "survives." If a beast is poorly designed, if the creator cannot answer questions or has made clear mistakes, the animal should be relegated (again by class vote) to another category called "extinct."

thumbs up	thumbs sideways	thumbs down
will survive	**may survive**	**extinct**

Answers

1-2. Are all boxes completed with sufficient, thoughtful detail?

4. Students show and tell about their fantasy creations.

Materials

☐ Construction materials. The variety of things you provide contains trade-offs. Fewer items will simplify classroom management. (Pencil and paper are sufficient.) More items encourage complex creative expression. Use materials that work for you.

☐ Scissors, construction paper, tape, glue, and staples can provide a basic three-dimensional modeling experience. Or your students might work with paper mache: flour plus water plus newspaper strips, molded over forms of crumpled paper and masking tape, balloons, chicken wire and the like. Additional items such as cardboard, clay, yarn, pipe cleaners, fabric scraps, rubber bands, clothespins, straight pins, bottle caps, buttons and paper clips may also be of use. Where possible, ask students to bring their own specialty items from home.

MEANWHILE, BACK IN THE JUNGLE

Complete the story below. Use all of the information that you have learned in order to survive. Intelligence is your only weapon; knowledge your only tool.

I had come to realize that I must leave the cave. It had sheltered me for the past weeks while my leg was on the mend. But my food and water were now gone.

Between me and the safety of my mountain village were many obstacles. Hungry lions were still in the tall grass, the river was full of crocodiles, and the forest beyond contained unknown danger.

I limped out into the bright warm sunlight . . .

...continue on another sheet of paper...

Objective

To summarize the survival concepts learned in this book. To communicate them in a creative story-writing activity.

Lesson Notes

Your students may continue writing this story exactly as stated, or they may alter the opening sentences. It should be at least two pages long (single spaced) for students 5th grade and over. Allow several days for completion, either as homework, or during times when other work is complete.

You may circle errors in grammar, syntax and punctuation, but emphasize that you will grade on content alone This helps remove the sense of frustration felt by students who write great stories, but have not yet mastered more technical language skills.

Getting students to write long stories may be more important than getting them to write perfectly. Grammar will improve as confidence, quality of ideas and expression improves. Ask student partners to trade story drafts, so they can correct spelling and grammar for each other They may not do a perfect job, but they will surely learn much. The final draft should then be recopied and turned in the next day.

Challenge your class to integrate, in creative ways, all or most of the survival strategies they have studied in this unit. Encourage them to write well to create excitement and complexity that will maintain high reading interest. Good science and good communication must happen together.

Answers

Student stories.

Materials

None.

SUPPLEMENTARY CUTOUTS

ADAPT-A-BIRD BODY PARTS

BODIES:

NECKS:

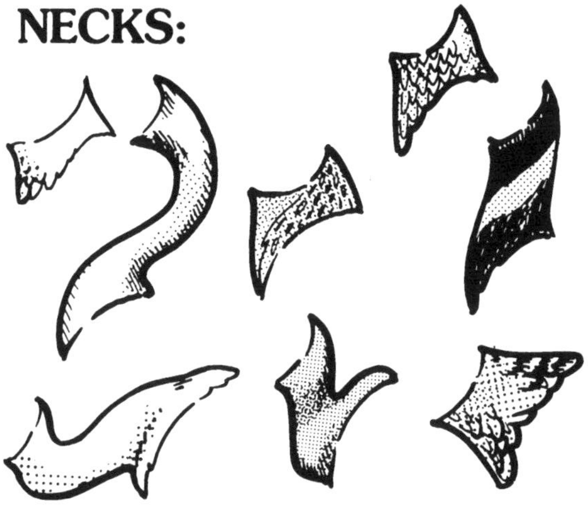

HEADS & BEAKS:

LEGS: (Don't cut apart)

Choose 1 body part from each box to make each bird.

TAILS:

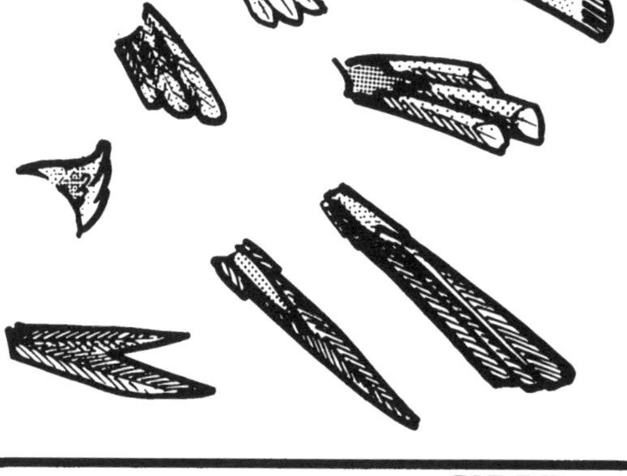

FEET:

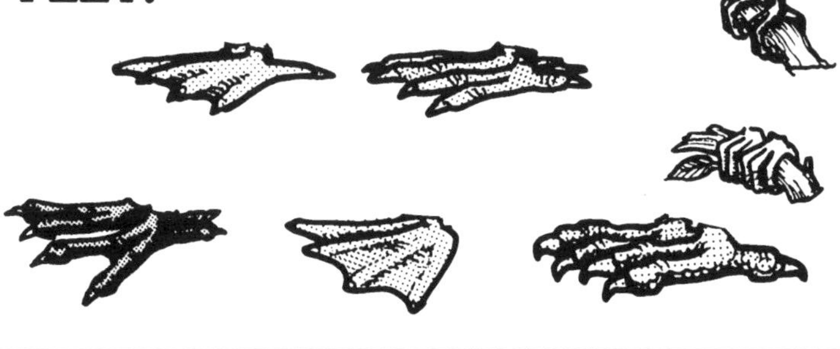

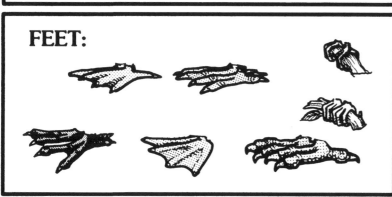

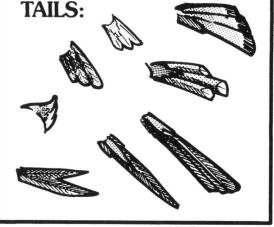

SELECTION SQUARES

for GET IT TOGETHER

HABITATS

YOU LIVE IN A WINDY PLACE	*YOU LIVE* IN A WET SWAMPY PLACE	*YOU LIVE* IN A DRY, DUSTY PLACE	*YOU LIVE* IN A USUALLY FROZEN PLACE	*YOU LIVE* ON AN ISLAND IN A SMALL LAKE
YOU LIVE IN EXTREMELY STEEP MOUNTAINS	*YOU LIVE* ON A FLAT GRASSY PRAIRIE	*YOU LIVE* IN A DEEP, THICK FOREST	*YOU LIVE* IN A STEAMY RAIN FOREST	*YOU LIVE* IN THE OCEAN
YOU LIVE NEAR A CORAL REEF	*YOU LIVE* ON THE BEACH	*YOU LIVE* IN A CITY, IN OLD BUILDINGS	*YOU LIVE* NEAR A LARGE HIGHWAY	*YOU LIVE* IN A SWIFT RIVER

SURVIVAL STRATEGIES

YOU SURVIVE BY PROTECTIVE COVERING	*YOU SURVIVE BY* SPEED	*YOU SURVIVE BY* WARNING COLORS	*YOU SURVIVE BY* MIMICRY	*YOU SURVIVE BY* CAMOUFLAGE
YOU SURVIVE BY PROTECTIVE COVERING	*YOU SURVIVE BY* SPEED	*YOU SURVIVE BY* WARNING COLORS	*YOU SURVIVE BY* MIMICRY	*YOU SURVIVE BY* CAMOUFLAGE
YOU SURVIVE BY PROTECTIVE COVERING	*YOU SURVIVE BY* SPEED	*YOU SURVIVE BY* WARNING COLORS	*YOU SURVIVE BY* MIMICRY	*YOU SURVIVE BY* CAMOUFLAGE

Feedback

If you enjoyed teaching TOPS please tell us so. Your praise motivates us to work hard. If you found an error or can suggest ways to improve this module, we need to hear about that too. Your criticism will help us improve our next new edition. Would you like information about our other publications? Ask us to send you our latest catalog free of charge.

For whatever reason, we'd love to hear from you. We include this self-mailer for your convenience.

Sincerely,

Ron & Peg

Ron and Peg Marson
author and illustrator

Your Message Here:

Module Title ______________________________ Date ____________________

Name ______________________________ School ____________________

Address ______________________________

City ______________________________ State ______ Zip ____________

FIRST FOLD

SECOND FOLD

RETURN ADDRESS

____

____

____

PLACE
STAMP
HERE

TOPS Learning Systems
342 S Plumas St
Willows, CA 95988

TAPE HERE

Made in the USA
Columbia, SC
18 April 2022

59119096R00037